THE
MAGIC
MIRROR

(no. 28)

THE MAGIC MIRROR

Dada and Surrealism
from a private collection

Elizabeth Cowling

SCOTTISH NATIONAL GALLERY OF MODERN ART

Published on the occasion of the exhibition
The Magic Mirror: Dada and Surrealism from a private collection
30 July–4 September 1988 at the Royal Scottish Academy, Edinburgh

Published by the Trustees of the National Galleries of Scotland
© the author and the Trustees of the National Galleries of Scotland, 1988
Illustrations for numbers 3, 8, 12, 16, 18, 19, 22, 24, 25, 29, 30,
31, 39, 40, 41, 65, 66, 68, 70, 72 and 74 are copyright DACS

ISBN 0 903148 81 1

Cover: René MAGRITTE, *Le miroir magique* (no. 39)

Designed by Cinamon and Kitzinger, London
Photographs by John Webb and Jack Mackenzie
Typeset by Wyvern Typesetting Ltd, Bristol
Printed in the Netherlands by Lecturis bv, Eindhoven

Foreword

For making this exhibition and accompanying publication possible we owe a profound debt of gratitude to the owner, who has agreed to part with nearly 200 paintings, drawings, prints, sculptures, books and periodicals for the best part of two months. This is the first time that the collection has been shown in public, although individual works have been lent to exhibitions in the past. We are confident that its breadth and richness will come as a revelation, and will give delight, to the vast majority of our visitors. Never before in Scotland has there been an opportunity to study Surrealist literature and artists' books in such depth. The exhibition of Edward James's collection (now dispersed) at the Gallery of Modern Art in 1976 contained none of this material which, as Elizabeth Cowling points out in her introductory essay, is essential to an understanding of Dada and Surrealism.

The exhibition has been organised by Richard Calvocoressi, Keeper of the Gallery of Modern Art. He has been assisted by Jonathan Mason, the Galleries' Registrar. We would like to thank Elizabeth Cowling, Lecturer at the University of Edinburgh and an acknowledged expert on Surrealism, for her readable, scholarly and informative catalogue. We hope that the owner, whose close association with the National Galleries of Scotland goes back more than a decade, will derive pleasure from this record of what is certainly a remarkable achievement in collecting.

TIMOTHY CLIFFORD
Director

Acknowledgements

Grateful thanks are due to David Gascoyne and Marcel Mariën for information about works by them in the collection; to David Sylvester and Sarah Whitfield of the Menil Foundation, London, for documentation on the three paintings by Magritte; to Matthew Gale for comments on de Chirico's drawings; to Dawn Ades, whose essays and entries in *Dada and Surrealism Reviewed*, 1978, remain invaluable; and to Simon Mason and Jonathan Livingstone for their co-operation. I am also grateful to Richard Calvocoressi for his unstinting support and help during the preparation of this catalogue, and to Alan Cowling for much needed editorial advice. Above all I am indebted to the collector, who has made the exhibition possible and the preparation of it a constant pleasure.

ELIZABETH COWLING
University of Edinburgh

(no. 159)

A PRIVATE VIEW

If there is one object in this collection which could be said to sum it up, that object would be Marcel Duchamp's *Boîte-en-valise* (no. 19). I say this for two reasons. The first is that Duchamp is the catalyst linking the three dominant strands in the collection – Dada, Surrealism and the early work of Paolozzi – animating the first, intervening in the second, influencing the third. The second is that the *Boîte-en-valise*, which is Duchamp's selective catalogue of his work, is on an intimate scale for the private connoisseur market, tailor-made to offer a distinctively private view of the things packed away so neatly and ingeniously inside its leather-bound carrying case. For the replicas of his works that Duchamp made for it are all miniatures; they can only be examined properly by one or perhaps two people at the same time; ideally they have to be unpacked by their owner slowly and carefully, one at a time, in the privacy of his or her own room, and then arranged correctly to form the mock museum display Duchamp intended. The experience is akin to unpacking a travelling case containing one's most precious possessions or to turning the pages of a rare and fragile illustrated book. And this collection, for all the presence of several major, public-scale masterpieces, is mainly a collection of small, portable things that best fit the private home – of modestly proportioned paintings and collages, of little-known sketches, of hand-size objects, of ephemera, of manuscripts and books. Like Duchamp's *Boîte-en-valise* it is in the true sense a private collection, offering a privileged, private view. Rarely does the spectator need to stand back; mostly he needs to get close; he ought to be able to touch and hold; he ought to be able to browse.

So, although one would dearly like to be able to name, and thus to honour publicly, the collector who has so astutely assembled all these precious things and so generously offered to share them with us, it is entirely in accord with the nature of the collection that the name should be withheld and the privacy respected.

Like all living collections this one has undergone various mutations. Many things have stayed, but others have been sold and replaced as the collector's taste and perspective have altered. Of those on view here (and we have the lion's share of the art collection) the first were acquired in 1962 and the last a quarter of a century later. The dynamic of that taste is revealed when we compare them: the oldest acquisitions are Lindner's *Solitary III* (no. 37), finished in 1962 and bought in that year, and Paolozzi and Kitaj's *Work in progress*, made in 1962 and bought in 1963 (no. 62); the newest are the *cadavre exquis* made by the Tanguys and the Bretons (no. 74), Laurence Vail's bottle (no. 76), Bellmer's gouache (no. 3), and Duchamp's *The Non-Dada* (no. 18) – all executed between 1922 and 1943, and all bought in 1987. In other words, Dada and

Surrealism were reached via Pop art. And this, broadly speaking, is what happened. In 1960 our collector, who had hitherto been interested in Old Master painting and fine antique furniture, silver and porcelain, went to Venice to see Peggy Guggenheim's marvellous collection of Surrealist and Abstract Expressionist art, and on the same visit was introduced to the work of Paolozzi on show at the Biennale. It took a few years for the experience to have a decisive effect on the collection, but in 1963 the first Paolozzis were acquired, to be followed over the years by many others – sketches, collages, prints and sculptures – as a close friendship between artist and collector developed. Paolozzi's interest in Dada and Surrealism is well known. He has made no secret of his debt or his sense of affinity. Through him and his work, as much as through the friendship with Peggy Guggenheim, the inclination to collect Dada and Surrealist art took definite form. *Türme* (no. 22), a curious, rather immature pre-Dada painting by Ernst, bought in 1963, led the way. Far more important Surrealist purchases followed within a few years: Picabia's *Sotileza* (no. 66) and Tanguy's *Jamais plus* (no. 73) in 1966, and in 1969 Ernst's *Max Ernst montrant à une jeune fille la tête de son père* (no. 25), arguably the highlight of the whole collection. In the 1970s the move in the direction of Dada and Surrealism was confirmed. Although more Paolozzis and the great early Bacon (no. 2; bought in 1979) were acquired, this was the decade for Delvaux's *Rue du tramway* (no. 16; bought in 1971), Man Ray's *Studio door* (no. 68; in 1973), Dalí's *Signal de l'angoisse* (no. 11; in 1974), and Picabia's *Fille née sans mère* (no. 65; in 1977). It was also the decade in which the library was created, in an extravagant, energetic campaign which has resulted in a truly rare hoard. (Space has, unfortunately, permitted only a limited display of this material.) In the 1980s the pace has inevitably slackened: prices have boomed, and the competition has vastly increased. Nevertheless, there have been notable acquisitions, including Magritte's *Miroir magique* (no. 39; bought in 1982), Giacometti's *Objet désagréable à jeter* (no. 29; in 1983), and Tanguy's *Ruban des excès* (no. 72; in 1984).

But the masters of Dada and Surrealism did not entirely oust artists of Paolozzi's generation, or artists of a younger generation still, where it seemed to the collector that there was an underlying affinity, a sensibility whose roots lay in the Dada–Surrealist tradition in twentieth-century art. Turnbull's beautiful *Metamorphosis I* (no. 75) was bought brand-new in 1982: the title alone makes a link with Surrealism – a movement dedicated to the concept of shifting identity and to the union of things which are dissimilar in nature, while the torso itself insistently reminds one of certain key late Duchamps which are not in the collection (especially *Given the illuminating gas and the waterfall*, 1948–49, a painted relief of a woman's nude body pitted all over with regular marks). The two John Davieses bought in 1980 (nos. 14 and 15) have a more indirect connection with Surrealism, but the emphasis on an intense gaze and the appeal to the spectator's inner vision betray the line of descent.

A readiness to experiment, an ability to see with a fresh eye and to draw connections between works of art which apparently lie outside the chosen field of the collection, is revealed in other purchases. The most unexpected of all the large-scale works is the Herbin *Composition* of 1919 (no. 32), which was bought in 1970. Herbin did not become a Surrealist, and he was never attracted to Dada. On the contrary, he is associated with the opposed, rationalist tendencies in French art of the post-First World War period – with on the one hand geometric abstraction, and on the other the 'classical revival'. But this Herbin suggests a figurative presence, looks like an elaborate collage, is dominated by irregular, cursively organic forms, strangely recalls Picabia's work of the *Udnie* phase (1913–14), and just as strangely seems to anticipate some typical Surrealist works of the 1930s. So, against the odds, it looks at home with the rest of the collection – a timely reminder to art historians that artists don't fit neatly into pre-determined categories, and that supposedly antithetical tendencies have much more common ground than is usually assumed.

The story of what has been and gone is further indication of the collector's discriminations. The first modern pictures to be acquired – even before the Lindner and the Paolozzis – belong to a quite different world. They included a late *Portrait of Gabrielle* by Renoir, and works by the great masters of Cubism – Picasso, Braque and Gris. All these were acquired in 1960–61. Together with a Kandinsky and a Léger bought in the mid-1960s, they were all sold because they no longer 'fitted'. The fate of the Magrittes is also instructive: *Perspective: Madame Récamier de Gérard*, 1950, an amusing transcription of the famous portrait by Gérard, in which Madame Récamier becomes a seated coffin, was purchased in 1970. But within three years it was being exchanged for the small but exceptionally fine Miró of 1927 (no. 42): Magritte's joke had worn rather thin, and the Miró plugged a serious gap. On the other hand two major Magrittes of the 'classic' period entered the collection – *La représentation*, 1937 (no. 41), purchased, like several other things, from Roland Penrose, the leader of British Surrealism and the owner of by far the greatest Surrealist collection in Britain, and *Le miroir magique*, 1929, an important but 'difficult' conundrum of a painting, which provocatively juxtaposes written word and image, and as such fits ideally into the distinctively Duchampian world of the collection.

I have written of the private nature of this collection. But it contains plenty of works which would be the envy of any 'big' collector or any museum. It is worth reflecting on a few of these. There is Picabia's *Fille née sans mère*, a characteristic example of his machine style of the 1915–18 period and of the nihilism and iconoclasm of the Dada movement as a whole. Implicitly comparing the illustration of locomotive wheels purloined from some mechanics' manual to a female divinity conceived immaculately, Picabia underlines his blasphemous intent through the use of a gold background normally reserved for icons and altarpieces. Or there is Ernst's *Max Ernst montrant à une jeune fille la tête de son père*, which summarises in one canvas many of the themes which obsessed the artist throughout his life – the Romantically menacing

German forest, the Oedipal rivalry with his father, the girl who is lover and muse – and which was important enough in André Breton's eyes to warrant inclusion in *Le Surréalisme et la peinture* in 1928. Or there is Giacometti's *Objet désagréable à jeter*, produced shortly after he joined the Surrealist movement, and exactly the kind of object-sculpture which set off the whole object-making craze of the 1930s – part-fetish, part-toy, a Sphinx's enigma if ever there was one, yet so nicely crafted that it is almost homely to the touch. Or there are the two Tanguys – typical of his most admired work, but without any of the fussy prolixity to which he is sometimes prone. Or there is the early Francis Bacon, which announces many of the themes developed in more celebrated later works, but which has an enigmatic and haunting quality redolent of the Surrealism of Ernst. Or there is Paolozzi and Kitaj's *Work in progress* – a commemoration of the stimulating artistic exchange between two of the foremost members of the British avant-garde when it was at its most vital in the early 1960s.

But these kinds of 'museum pieces' are outnumbered by the smaller, more personal works. The Schwitters collage (no. 70) is a fine example of his *Merz* style, but it is an intimate piece which must be looked at close to, and it was in fact made for a friend. The rapid pen and ink drawing by de Chirico (no. 8), which shows him in unusually playful mode, is also the kind of drawing he might have given away. (Lucian Freud's deftly naive sketch, no. 26, for *The painter's room* is in the same category of light and informal drawing.) Then there is Hannah Höch's photomontage (no. 33) – crisply satirical, apparently off hand, but so strong in its abstract design that we are reminded of the links between German Dada and Constructivism. Or the Grosz postcard (no. 31), surely never intended to be anything other than a private joke, and yet encapsulating so much of the irreverence intrinsic to the Dadaist spirit. And Duchamp's *Non-Dada*, sent as a sly gift to Man Ray, and inevitably – since everything Duchamp touched seems instantly to have become a kind of sacred relic – labelled and preserved for posterity. Or there is the ultra-refined, Valentine-like drawing Hans Bellmer presented to the adolescent poetess Gisèle Prassinos (no. 3). Or the scrapbook assembled for his own pleasure by David Gascoyne, who as a teenage boy wrote some of the best Surrealist poetry to come out of Britain, and who won the trust and admiration of no less a person than André Breton (no. 28). The list of these works which may be small and ephemeral but which have historical significance and their own explosive charge could go on and on.

With the scrapbook and the Grosz postcard and the drawing for Gisèle Prassinos we find ourselves in the realm of the manuscript, and thus at the private core of this private collection. Nothing can bring one closer to the heart of an artist's work than the sketchbook or the notebook. Nothing can bring one closer to the heart of movements like Dada or Surrealism than the periodicals, the manifestos, the signed and dedicated copies of books, the letters and the manuscripts, which bear witness to the constant interchange of ideas and the constant effort to win converts to the cause. Had the collection been formed by an erstwhile member of either movement it would not be surprising to find a certain amount of this private material. But it was not. That we should find so many mementoes of the day-to-day life of these men and women is testimony to a special insight and understanding.

Among the manuscripts in the collection the most important are probably those involving Dalí. There is his draft scenario for a documentary film on Surrealism, illustrated with idiosyncratic diagrams summarising and interpreting the theories of Freud (no. 93). Very likely this scheme was proposed by Breton in recognition of Dalí's experience as a film-maker and as part of the general effort in the 1930s to make Surrealism a truly international and universal movement. But in any case it proved abortive. There is also a fascinating and highly significant correspondence of a less harmonious nature between Breton and Dalí, documenting Breton's suspicions about Dalí's politics and the sincerity of his allegiance to Surrealism, his serious misgivings about some of Dalí's new paintings, including *The enigma of William Tell*, and his repeated efforts to coerce Dalí into making more regular and more orthodox contributions to Surrealist manifestations (no. 88). This correspondence also sheds light on the political tensions of the 1930s and on Breton's internationalist aspirations.

In contrast to the private manuscripts the library also contains a comprehensive collection of the major reviews of the Dada and Surrealist movements – *291, The Blind Man, 391, La Révolution Surréaliste, Le Surréalisme au Service de la Révolution, Minotaure* and *VVV*, to name the most influential. These represented the public voice, and a knowledge of them is literally indispensable to an understanding of Dada and Surrealism, which were both dedicated to vociferous intervention in the public sphere, to theorising and proselytising. Except for *Minotaure*, which was distributed in Britain through Zwemmer's in the Charing Cross Road, these reviews are in themselves exceedingly rare, absent from practically all British public libraries and inaccessible except in recent reprints. To be able to study at first hand the flamboyantly eccentric typography and layout of *291* or *391*, or the mock-scientific, studiedly dull typography and layout of *La Révolution Surréaliste*, is a great privilege. The potent visual impact of the magazines closes the gap between our era and theirs, brings alive again the urgent debates that animated them, banishes the anodyne effect of academic history.

Books inevitably form the main part of the library. But Dada and Surrealist books were frequently collaborative ventures between writers and artists, so the relationship between the library and the art collection is a close one. In several of the heroes of the art collection – Picabia, Duchamp, Schwitters, de Chirico, Dalí, Ernst and Paolozzi – we have artists for whom writing (in however unconventional a form) was a very significant activity, artists who expressed their determination to appeal to the mind as much as to the eye not simply through creating works of a cerebral character, but through the production of manifestos, books, reviews, and so forth. Indeed in Dada and Surrealism the ideal had always been the union of visual and verbal – *peinture-poésie*. This ideal was expressed in numerous ways: in the marriage of text and image in the periodicals; in the inclusion of words or phrases in paintings; in the creation of a mixed genre like the collage novel, which is read, but read in images; in the creation of objects, collages etc. by the poets, and of poems and texts by the painters; and above all in the production of illustrated books, in which the images exist on terms of equality with the text, enhancing, complementing and extending its impact. Tristan Tzara's *vingt-cinq poèmes*, published in Zurich in 1918 (no. 144), establishes the pattern: his text and Arp's abstract woodcut illustrations are printed uniformly on the page, creating a perfectly integrated visual effect and testifying to the harmony between writer and artist.

Of all the painters Ernst was the one who took illustration most seriously, designing bindings and experimenting with unusual printmaking processes in the search for the ideal reproductive form for his drawings. He was a great reader, on close terms with the poets in the movement, a bibliophile with a fine library of his own, and a painter whose work has an unashamedly literary character. His relationship with Eluard was particularly fertile. They met in 1921 even before he moved to Paris, and collaborated on *Répétitions*, a book of poems and collages which is in a real sense the forerunner of Ernst's own collage novels of the 1929–34 period. On subsequent occasions Ernst supplied pen and ink drawings, lithographs and etchings to accompany Eluard's poems (e.g. nos. 99–101). A love of books united them, and for Eluard book collecting and book production were a passion, even a necessity. (It is typical of him that when times were hard he could bring himself to sell off his art collection, but never his books.) He, perhaps more than anyone else in the Surrealist movement, was determined to keep alive the nineteenth-century French tradition of the *beau livre*, and was responsible for initiating several major de luxe publications and encouraging new partnerships between poets and painters.

A devoted friend of Eluard's and another true bibliophile was Georges Hugnet. Hugnet is hardly known to us in Britain, yet he was a very important figure in the movement during the 1930s, which is without question the great period of the Surrealist book. He is one of the principal forces in this collection, for it contains many things dispersed from his library after his death in 1974, including an elaborate suite of unpublished collages apparently laid out to receive a text (no. 35). Hugnet ran a small bookbinding studio in Paris during the 1930s and at the same time acted as a kind of book-buyer for his friends, tracking down for them rare volumes on often esoteric subjects. On excellent terms with Duchamp, Hugnet shared Duchamp's obsession with fine craftsmanship and, like Duchamp, designed unique covers for books in his own collection and for books for his friends. Their sympathy for each other is recorded in several of the most important items in this library. The *Boîte-en-valise* and the *Green box* (no. 96) exhibited here were both made for Hugnet, and have special dedications to him. And there is a small cache of letters from Duchamp about the making of the first *Boîte-en-valise* (no. 97). Hugnet was also close to Bellmer, with whom he collaborated on the exquisite, if louche, *Œillades ciselées en branche* (no. 117), and on *Les Jeux de la Poupée* (no. 85). Displayed are Hugnet's own copy of the former (for which he made a special protective leather box, stamped provocatively on the spine with the abbreviated title *Œillades* – bunches/lascivious glances), and his handwritten draft translations of Bellmer's text for the latter. Another of his special friends was Oscar Dominguez, the inventor of the *decalcomania* technique. Perhaps the most beautifully crafted book in the whole collection is Hugnet's own specially printed and specially bound copy of *Le Feu au cul* (no. 116), a privately printed, very exclusive publication – only 53 copies in all – and a characteristic example of Surrealist erotica. It is 'prefaced' with a suite of etchings by Dominguez, and Hugnet's text is overprinted in colour with Dominguez's schematised drawings of copulating couples. Pocket-size, *Le Feu au cul* resembles the smallest sketchbook or autograph book. Hugnet has bound it in cream-coloured leather and made decalcomania endpapers for it, and on the cover, in purple line, is impressed a simplified reproduction of one of Dominguez's drawings. To protect the book Hugnet has made a bamboo-coloured folder, lined in mushroom-coloured suede. And this and the book enclosed within it fit tightly but smoothly into a hard, bamboo-coloured, leather-trimmed slip-case, which is itself lined in a soft, pure white material. The alliance of meticulous, time-consuming craftsmanship with 'convulsive' sexuality enshrines a paradox which is itself a mirror of the supreme Surrealist goal of the 'reconciliation of opposites'.

In accord with the tradition of the *beau livre*, virtually all Surrealist books were produced in limited editions, and within any given edition there was usually a small de luxe special printing on expensive handmade papers: these copies were intended for connoisseurs, and there was often in addition a handful of *hors commerce* copies for the friends of the author and his illustrator. Many of the copies in this collection are from these special printings, and several are the 'first' copies containing the original manuscripts (e.g. nos. 86 and 126). Most of the books on display have inscriptions or dedications of some sort, and several have original drawings or additional states of etchings. For instance the copy of a rather little-known book of poems by Alice Paalen has not only the deleted proof of Miró's frontispiece etching, but a fine pencil and crayon drawing by him on the title-page (no. 124). (This is another of the many relics of Hugnet's library.) All these last-minute interventions give us a moving sense of the intimate life of these 'historic' figures and a clearer perspective on the movement to which they belonged, an insight into their allegiances and into the intricate network of relationships that determined its development.

Indeed for anyone interested in the inner as well as the outer life of the individuals and the movements represented, this collection is the perfect open sesame.

CATALOGUE

Paintings, Sculpture, and Works on Paper

Dimensions are in centimetres, height before width. Books, periodicals etc. have been measured unopened. Square brackets are used where the title of a work is uncertain.

EILEEN AGAR born 1899

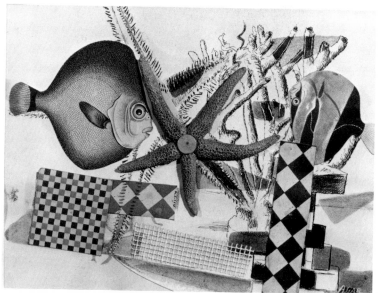

1. Fish circus *1939*
Collage and watercolour on paper, 18.5 × 25
Inscribed 'AGAR' b.r.

Having studied at the Slade and in Paris in the late 1920s, Agar began to move in Surrealist circles in London in 1935. Under this influence she started to experiment with innovative techniques, working by preference with mixed media and collage. She became a prominent member of the English Surrealist group and was represented in the International Surrealist exhibitions held in London in 1936, Paris in 1938, and Amsterdam in 1939, as well as in *Fantastic art. Dada. Surrealism* organised by the Museum of Modern Art in New York in 1936–37. Her delight in using natural found objects, such as the starfish pinned onto this work, was shared by other English Surrealists, in particular Paul Nash.

FRANCIS BACON born 1909

2. Figure study I
1945–46
Oil on canvas, 123 × 105.5
Not inscribed
COLOUR PLATE

A key early painting, *Figure study I* was first exhibited in February 1946 at the Lefevre Gallery, London. It relates closely to the slightly larger, explicitly figurative *Figure study II*, 1945–46, in which the same tweed coat recurs in a similar position. The abrupt juxtaposition of coat, hat, and flowering plant has analogies with Surrealist imagery, and Bacon's handling of the coat may be compared with Ernst's use of *frottage* and *grattage* (rubbing and scraping techniques).

HANS BELLMER 1902–75

3. Untitled *1936*
Ink, gouache and collage on black paper, 24 × 19
Inscribed 'À GISÈLE/
PRASSINOS/AVEC LES
HOMMAGES/DE HANS
BELLMER' *c.r.*

Early in 1935 Bellmer visited Paris and was welcomed into the Surrealist group, where he enjoyed the particular support of Eluard. Photographs of his dismembered and rearranged *Doll* had already appeared in the sixth issue of *Minotaure* in the winter of 1934–35 under the title 'Variations on the montage of an articulated minor' (see no. 83). In 1936 he was invited by the Surrealists to do a frontispiece drawing for a short story by Gisèle Prassinos, a fourteen-year-old poetess who, as the archetypal *femme-enfant*, was the group's adored child prodigy and muse. With his well-known predilection for adolescent girls Bellmer was the inevitable choice as illustrator for her work: this drawing commemorates their mutual admiration, for Prassinos dedicated several of her writings to him.

15

4. Untitled *1938 or 1939*
Pencil on paper, 12 × 9
Not inscribed

This is a drawing for one of the illustrations to Hugnet's *Œillades ciselées en branche*, published in Paris in March 1939 (see no. 117).

ANDRÉ BRETON 1896–1966

LE DÉCLIN DE LA SOCIÉTÉ BOURGEOISE

5. Le déclin de la
société bourgeoise
*(The decay of
bourgeois society)*
date unknown
Collage, 13.5 × 8.5
Inscribed 'A B' b.l.

Although Breton confessed to total incompetence in the practice of art, like other poets in the Surrealist movement he made a number of collages and objects, most of which date from the 1930s. Indeed, it was he who, as early as 1924, had called for the creation and circulation of objects seen in dreams – a suggestion which did not bear fruit until 1930-31, when the 'object craze' overtook the whole Surrealist movement. He was also an active participant in the *cadavre exquis* (exquisite corpse) game (see no. 74).

EDWARD BURRA 1905–76

6. Honky-tonk girl
1929
Pen and ink on paper,
55.5 × 38
Inscribed 'E. J. Burra 1929'
b.r.

Closely related to many of his contemporary paintings and drawings depicting cabarets, bars and night-spots, *Honky-tonk girl* reflects not only Burra's delight in popular culture but his particular admiration for the brilliant satirical drawings of Grosz published in *Ecce Homo* in Berlin in 1923.

16

7. [Racecourse collage]
1930
Gouache, ink, pencil and
collage on paper, 62 × 50
Not inscribed

This is no. 59 in A. Causey's *Edward Burra. Complete catalogue*, Oxford, 1985. A wittily observant treatment of a day out at the races, it has marked iconographic and stylistic affinities with the collages of the German Dadaists and the contemporary collage work of the Surrealists. Although he was too independent and individualistic to become an orthodox member of the group, Burra showed regularly with the Surrealists in the late 1930s. He was, for example, represented by several of his collages in the International Surrealist exhibitions held in London and Paris in 1936 and 1938.

8. Le rêve mystérieux
(The mysterious dream)
c. 1913
Ink on paper, 20.5 × 13.5
Inscribed 'Le rêve
mystérieux.' *b.c.*

This drawing was reproduced as the frontispiece to Henri Pastoureau's *Le Corps trop grand pour un cerceuil*, a collection of poems published in 1936 with a preface by Breton (see no. 126). Like a closely related drawing, *L'apparition du cheval*, reproduced in the very first issue of *La Révolution Surréaliste*, it was not, apparently, translated into a painting. It represents exactly the kind of dream-like image from de Chirico's first stay in Paris (1911–15) that Breton and his Surrealist colleagues particularly admired, and that decisively influenced the development of Ernst, Tanguy, Dalí and Magritte.

SALVADOR DALÍ born 1904

9. [Composition
with skeleton] *1934*
Etching, 32 × 20
Inscribed 'Dalí' *b.r.*

10. [Composition with
chair and inkstand] *1934*
Etching, 21 × 20
Inscribed 'Dalí' *b.r.*

These are among the etchings Dalí made for a new edition of the Comte de Lautréamont's *Les Chants de Maldoror* published in 1934 (see no. 121). Only about half the projected number of copies of the book were actually printed, and the unused impressions were signed by Dalí at a later stage. These two images appear between pages 22 and 23, and at the top of page 37, respectively.

11. Le signal
de l'angoisse
(The signal of anguish)
1936
Oil on wood panel,
21.5 × 16
Inscribed '"Le Signal de
l'angoisse"/Dalí 1936' on
back of panel

This painting passed directly from the artist to the Galerie Kaethe Perls in Paris, and from there to the Frank Perls Gallery in Hollywood. According to Klaus Perls it was begun at least by 1934, the finishing touches and the inscription being added in 1936. A fine example of the exquisite, miniaturist style of the early 1930s which earned Dalí such success and notoriety in America, it does not, however, employ the 'Paranoiac-critical method' Dalí had first 'discovered' in 1929–30, in which objects are susceptible to multiple readings and are in a perpetual, but controlled, state of metamorphosis.

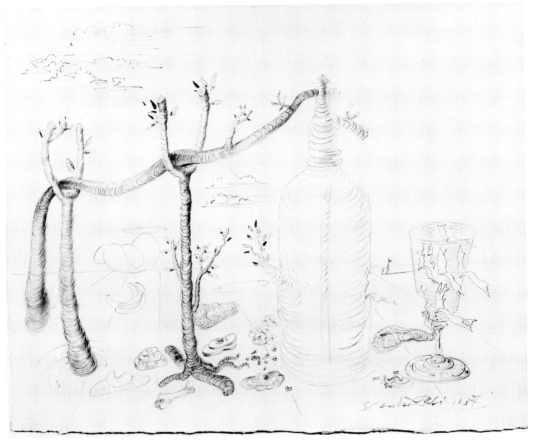

12. [Surrealist
composition with a
soda siphon] *1937*
Pen and ink and gouache
on paper, 44 × 54
Inscribed 'Salvador Dalí 1937'
b.r.

This drawing, which was until recently in the collection of Edward James, one of the most important British patrons of Surrealism and a particular admirer of Dalí, is closely related to an oil painting of the same date. It explores one of Dalí's favourite motifs: the hard, strictly utilitarian object which has gone as soft as melted Gruyère cheese.

13. [Composition with figures and the skeleton of a boat]
c. 1938
Pen and ink on paper,
26 × 44.5
Not inscribed

Like no. 12, this drawing was originally in the Edward James collection. The motifs of the skeletal boat and the women with crutches appear in a number of paintings of the 1930s.

JOHN DAVIES born 1946

14. Drawing of P.D.
1979
Pastel and pencil on paper,
49.5 × 39
Not inscribed

Included in the British Council exhibition of Davies's work which toured to Hamburg, Duisburg and Karlsruhe in 1981–82.

15. Head No. 30
1979–80
Mixed media, h. 20
Inscribed '30' on base

Davies studied at Hull, Manchester and the Slade before winning a sculpture fellowship to Gloucester College of Art in 1969. In 1970 he won the Sainsbury Award. His first one-man show was held at the Whitechapel Art Gallery in 1972. This work was first exhibited in his one-man show at Marlborough Fine Art, London, in November–December 1980.

PAUL DELVAUX born 1897

16. La rue du tramway
(Street of the trams)
1938–39
Oil on canvas, 90 × 130.5
Inscribed 'P. DELVAUX/1–39'
b.r., and 'à ma chère/Suzanne'
on back of canvas
COLOUR PLATE

Delvaux never participated formally in the Surrealist movement, although he was adopted by it and, from 1936 onwards, was directly influenced by the 'illusionistic' paintings of Dalí, Ernst and Magritte. This frequently exhibited picture has been known by a variety of alternative titles, including 'La rue', 'L'arrière-saison', and 'Le tramway'. (For fuller details see M. Butor, J. Clair and S. Houbart-Wilkin, *Delvaux. Catalogue de l'œuvre peint*, Brussels, 1975, no. 94.) First shown in the Palais des Beaux-Arts in Brussels in 1940, it was reproduced in the English Surrealist periodical *London Bulletin*, nos. 18–20, in June 1940. Its first owners were P. G. Van Hecke, the important Brussels dealer-collector, and his wife, Norine, a leading couturière for whom Magritte made publicity designs. Industrialised cityscapes, railways, stations and sidings had been dominant themes in Delvaux's early realist work (1922–23), returning in the dream-like Surrealist scenarios of the late 1930s, of which *La rue du tramway* is a fine example. Characteristically it combines potent reminiscences of the Metaphysical paintings of de Chirico with those of Italian Renaissance art.

17. Nu au jardin *(Nude in the garden) 1966*
Pen and ink and watercolour on paper, 62 × 50
Inscribed 'P. DELVAUX/ST. IDESBALD/10–8–66' *b.r.*

The importance Delvaux himself attached to this drawing is reflected in the fact that he chose it for illustration in *Les dessins de Paul Delvaux*, published by Denoël in 1967 (p. 105). The title used above is the one given in that book.

MARCEL DUCHAMP 1887–1968

18. The Non-Dada
1922
Found object: paper, 14 × 11
Inscribed on attached flap of envelope 'The Non-Dada – affectueusement Rrose' *in Duchamp's hand, and* '(Man Ray collection)' *in Man Ray's hand*

The object Duchamp has appropriated is a 48-page religious pamphlet published by vocational pupils at the 'School of the Four C's' (Caney Creek Community Center, Pippopass, Knott County, Kentucky, April–May 1922). He found it in New York, added the title and greetings, and then sent it to Man Ray, who had moved to Paris in the summer of 1921. It was included in the Duchamp retrospective exhibition held in the Tate Gallery in 1966 (no. 196).

19. Boîte-en-valise
(Box in a suitcase)
1935–41
Leather-covered case
containing miniature replicas,
photographs, and colour
reproductions of works by
Duchamp, 40.5 × 38 × 10
Inscribed inside 'pour
Georges Hugnet ce no II/
de vingt boîtes-en-valise
contenant/chacune 69 items
et un original/et par Marcel
Duchamp/Paris mai 1941'
Reproduction on celluloid of
The large glass *incised*
'coloriage original/Marcel
Duchamp/1940' *b.r.*
COLOUR PLATE

This is no. II of the de luxe edition of twenty *Boîtes-en-valise*, out of a total production which Duchamp stipulated was not to exceed 320. Duchamp worked from 1935–40 in Paris on the material for his 'portable museum', assembling photographs, supervising the meticulous colour reproductions of his works and procuring replicas of three of the ready-mades, including the notorious *Fountain* (urinal). Pride of place in the eventual lay-out of the works was to be given to his masterpiece, *The bride stripped bare by her bachelors, even*, which was reproduced on a sheet of transparent celluloid. During the German occupation of France, Duchamp, armed with a cheese merchant's identity card which enabled him to move in and out of the occupied zone, transported the facsimiles to Marseilles, from where they were shipped safely to New York (see no. 97). He himself returned to New York in 1942. Individual valises were assembled over the years by Duchamp and various assistants, including Joseph Cornell. Twelve additional works were included in those assembled after 1955. There were several precedents in Duchamp's work for this kind of bulk production, in particular *The green box* of 1934 (see no. 96). In conversation with J. J. Sweeney in 1955, Duchamp commented: 'Here again a new form of expression was involved. Instead of painting something new, my aim was to reproduce the paintings and the objects I liked and collect them in a space as small as possible. I did not know how to go about it. I first thought of a book, but I did not like the idea. Then it occurred to me that it could be a box in which all my works would be collected and mounted like in a small museum, a portable museum, so to speak'. It has been suggested that he may well have been spurred on in this enterprise by the sense of impending disaster that afflicted Europe in the years before the outbreak of the Second World War.

20. Feuille de
vigne femelle
(Female fig leaf)
1950/61
Bronze, 9 × 14 × 12.5
Inscribed 'Feuille de Vigne
femelle/Marcel Duchamp
1951' *on base*

Duchamp made two original casts in galvanised plaster in 1950, keeping one for himself and giving the other to Man Ray when the latter left New York in 1951. Using the cast in his possession, Man Ray organised a first edition of ten in painted plaster in Paris in 1951. The present bronze is from the edition of eight bronze casts made in 1961 by the Galerie Rive Droite in Paris. Questioned by Pierre Cabanne on the place of eroticism in his work, Duchamp replied that it was: 'Enormous. Visible or conspicuous, or, at any rate, underlying. . . . I believe in eroticism a lot, because it's truly a rather widespread thing throughout the world, a thing that everyone understands. It replaces, if you wish, what other literary schools called Symbolism, Romanticism. It could be another "ism", so to speak. . . . If eroticism is used as a principal basis, a principal end, then it takes the form of an "ism", in the sense of a school. . . . To be able to reveal them [things that are usually hidden], and to place them at everyone's disposal – I think this is important because it's the basis of everything, and no one talks about it. Eroticism was a theme, even an "ism", which was the basis of everything I was doing at the time of the "Large Glass". It kept me from being obliged to return to already existing theories, aesthetic or otherwise' (*Dialogues with Marcel Duchamp*, London, 1971, p. 88).

21. Coin de chasteté
(Wedge of chastity)
1954/63
Bronze and dental plastic,
5.5 × 8.5 × 4.2
Inscribed 'Coin de chasteté/M. Duchamp 54' *on base of bronze*
Inscribed 'EDITION DE LA GALERIE/SCHWARZ MILAN/ EXEMPLAIRE POUR/ MARCEL/DUCHAMP/⁰⁄₈' *on base of plastic*

An edition of eight signed and numbered replicas in bronze and dental plastic was issued by the Galleria Schwarz in Milan in 1963. This is the *hors commerce* cast made for Duchamp himself. The original of this object was made in galvanised plaster and dental plastic. On their wedding day (New York, 16 January 1954), Duchamp gave it to his wife Teeny. He explained to Pierre Cabanne: 'It was my wedding present to her. We still have it on our table. We usually take it with us, like a wedding ring, no?' (*Dialogues with Marcel Duchamp*, p. 88). However, in *The Almost Complete Works of Marcel Duchamp*, Arts Council of Great Britain, 1966, no. 176, *Coin de chasteté* is dated 1951–52, that is, just later than *Feuille de vigne femelle* and another closely related erotic object, *Objet-Dard*, of 1951. This dating was apparently sanctioned by Duchamp himself.

MAX ERNST 1891–1976

22. Türme *(Towers)*
1914
Oil on canvas, 60 × 43
Inscribed 'Max Ernst 1916' *b.l.*
ILLUSTRATED OVERLEAF

Although many critics, including Werner Spies (*Max Ernst. Œuvre-Katalog*, Houston, Texas, Menil Foundation, and Cologne, DuMont, 1975, no. 252), have accepted the dating in the inscription, according to John Russell (*Max Ernst. Life and Work*, London, 1967, p. 344) this picture was painted in 1914 before Ernst was mobilised. This dating seems plausible, because the picture relates closely to another important abstracted and geometricised canvas which is inscribed 1914, *Composition with the letter E*. The imagery of chimneys, rooftops and towers may owe something to the work of Delaunay, which was well-known in Germany before the war, but *Türme* also anticipates some of the Dadaist works Ernst executed in Cologne in 1919–20, such as *Fruit of a long experience* and *Small machine constructed by minimax dadamax himself* . . . , which are dominated by tall and precariously assembled tower-like structures.

23. Untitled *1921*
Collage on paper mounted on paperboard, 12 × 10
Inscribed 'M.e' *b.r.*

Dated 1921 by Spies (op. cit., no. 460). For this, as for many other collages executed in Cologne in 1920–21, Ernst cannibalised popular – usually outdated – manuals and magazines profusely illustrated with engravings of machines, instruments, appliances etc. The irrational scenarios evoked by these unprecedented juxtapositions were paralleled in contemporary

(no. 22)

paintings such as *The Elephant Celebes*, now in the Tate Gallery. It was these works that attracted the admiration of the Parisian Dadaists, and early in 1922 Ernst settled in Paris, quickly becoming a leading participant in the nascent Surrealist group.

24. La femme au parapluie/Femme assise à l'ombrelle *(Woman with an umbrella)*
c. 1921
Oil, gouache, crayon and pencil on board, 16.5 × 10 (excluding frame)
Not inscribed

Dated *c.* 1921 by Spies (op. cit., no. 416), which on internal grounds seems wholly convincing, this important little painting has passed through the hands of a number of key figures within the Surrealist movement in France and England, including Paul Eluard, Roland Penrose and Edouard and Sybil Mesens. In the almost fetishistic emphasis on feminine clothing and accoutrements, typical of this and other works of 1920–21, one can detect the influence of Max Klinger, the German Symbolist artist whose story-in-pictures *Paraphrase on the finding of a glove* (published in 1881) Ernst greatly admired.

25. Max Ernst montrant à une jeune fille la tête de son père *(Max Ernst showing a girl the head of his father)*
1926 or 1927
Oil on canvas, 114 × 146.5
Inscribed 'Max Ernst' *b.l.*
COLOUR PLATE

Dated 1927 by Spies (op. cit., no. 1169), this painting was first exhibited in Ernst's one-man show in the Galerie Van Leer, Paris, in March–April 1927, and a couple of months later in his show at the Galerie Le Centaure in Brussels. It was chosen by Breton for reproduction in his important early essay on Surrealist painting, *Le Surréalisme et la peinture* (Paris, 1928), where it is dated 1926. It was long in the collection of the Belgian abstract painter Victor Servranckx. *Max Ernst montrant . . .* represents a rather unusual combination of two normally alternative manners employed by Ernst after he settled in Paris:

a pseudo-Mannerist figurative style seen frequently in 1923–24, which resurfaces intermittently in 1926 and 1927 (e.g. in the blasphemous *The Virgin spanking the infant Christ before three witnesses*, 1926), and the 'automatic' *grattage* (scraping) style employed from 1925, notably in the great sequence of *Forests* painted in 1927. Its importance in Ernst's eyes is reflected in the fact that he alluded to it in his account of his recent work in 'Au-delà de la peinture', an autobiographical essay written in 1936. Ernst has just been describing his discovery of the technique of *frottage* (rubbing), its relationship to automatic writing, his 'passivity' when creating, and his desire to become a 'seer'. He continues: 'C'est alors que je me suis vu moi-même, *montrant à une jeune fille la tête de mon père.* La terre ne trembla que mollement' (It was then that I saw myself, *showing to a girl the head of my father.* The earth quivered only gently).

LUCIAN FREUD born 1922

26. Untitled *1943*
Black and coloured crayons on paper, 14 × 22
Not inscribed

A study for *The painter's room* (1943, oil on canvas). The juxtaposition in the latter of a huge zebra's head projecting through a window, the potted palm, a sofa and scattered articles of clothing, results in a dream-like surrealistic image reminiscent of such paintings by Ernst as *Oedipus Rex*, 1922. However, the zebra's head was in fact a stuffed one which Freud had brought home 'as a substitute for the live horses whose company he had grown to love while living in the country' (J. Russell, in *Lucian Freud*, Arts Council of Great Britain, 1974, p. 18).

27. [Head of a boy with a book], *c. 1944*
Black and coloured crayons on dark grey paper, 48 × 30.5
Not inscribed

The drawing relates closely to *Boy with a pigeon* (1944) and to another drawing of a boy, probably the same model, which is inscribed 20 January 1944.

DAVID GASCOYNE born 1916

28. Scrapbook *c. 1940–44*
25.5 × 19
FRONTISPIECE

Gascoyne was a prominent member of the Surrealist group in England. While living in France he had written a manifesto announcing the formation of an English branch of the movement, which was published in French in *Cahiers d'Art* in 1935. In the same year, with help and advice from Breton, Eluard and Péret, he published *A Short Survey of Surrealism*, which offered a full and lucid account of the movement up to the present and which remains to this day a classic insider history. The scrapbook was compiled as a personal record of the Surrealist movement, especially in its English manifestation. As well as drawings etc. by Gascoyne himself, and press cuttings reviewing *inter alia* the International Surrealist exhibition held in London in 1936, it contains numerous rare tracts, catalogues, and printed ephemera. It was given to Zwemmer, the London book dealer, just after the war in payment for books which Gascoyne had purchased.

ALBERTO GIACOMETTI 1901–66

29. Objet désagréable à jeter *(Disagreeable object to be disposed of) 1931*
Wood, 23 × 25 × 27
Not inscribed
COLOUR PLATE

Giacometti's presence in the Surrealist group during the years 1930–35 was one of the principal factors in establishing sculpture, or, more properly, the object, as a central creative concern within the movement as a whole. Breton regarded his *Suspended ball*, 1930–31, as a seminal work, and purchased a wooden version from which he was never parted. *Objet désagréable à jeter* was among the seven works reproduced in drawings to accompany a short poetic text, 'Objets mobiles et muets', which Giacometti published in *Le Surréalisme au Service de la Révolution* no. 3, December 1931, pp. 18–19 (no. 170). Although, unlike several other of his sculpture-objets, including *Suspended ball*, it does not have moving parts, it is meant to be manipulated and played with, and it can come to rest in several different positions. Indeed, in another of the illustrations to the same text, Giacometti depicts a hand touching another object-sculpture of similar type – a phallic, barbed and tusk-like form. No. 29 was for many years in the collection of Roland Penrose, who had purchased it directly from the artist. It has sometimes been dated 1935 and titled 'Objet sans base' (Object without a base). There is also a version in bronze.

30. Untitled *c. 1932*
Pen and ink on paper,
32×× 24
Not inscribed

Formerly in the collection of Edward James, this drawing appears to have been the one Giacometti prepared for reproduction in line in *Minotaure* nos. 3–4, December 1933, p. 78, where it is published in the middle of an article by Igor Markevitch, 'La Musique est l'art de recréer le monde dans le domaine des sons'. It relates closely to Giacometti's important Surrealist sculpture, *Woman with her throat cut*, 1932, of which a cast is in the collection of the Scottish National Gallery of Modern Art.

GEORGE GROSZ 1893–1959

31. Untitled *1923*
Collage on postcard of
Titian's Entombment,
8.5 × 13.5
Inscribed 'sammelt
anssichtskarten !!!!' *b.c.,*
and 'George Grosz' *on*
back of card

Grosz sent the duly amended postcard of Titian's *Entombment* (Musée de Louvre, Paris) to Georg Scholtz, who was a close friend and a mentor. It is postmarked 1 March 1923. The photomontage procedure, used so casually and amusingly here, had been 'invented' by the Berlin Dadaists during the First World War. Although Raoul Hausmann and Hannah Höch made a rival claim, Grosz asserted that it was he and John Heartfield who, in 1916, invented the technique: 'On a piece of

cardboard we pasted a mishmash of advertisements for hernia belts, student song books and dog food, labels from schnaps and wine bottles, and photographs from picture papers, cut up at will in such a way as to say, in pictures, what would have been banned by the censors if we had said it in words. In this way we made postcards supposed to have been sent home from the Front, or from home to the Front' (Grosz quoted by H. Richter in *Dada. Art and anti-art*, London, 1965, p. 117). Those 'postcards' – direct ancestors of this collage – were among the first Dada photomontages. But it is also worth noting that among the precedents for the photomontage technique as practised by the Dadaists were the many comic picture postcards, dating from the turn of the century, which consisted of composite photographs: favourite photographic jokes of the postcard designers included the grotesquely altered famous work of art, and the enlarged head on a diminutive body.

AUGUSTE HERBIN 1882–1960

32. Composition
(Composition), 1919
Oil on canvas, 73 × 91.5
Inscribed 'herbin nov. 1919'
b.r.

Herbin was one of the circle of artists who exhibited in the avant-garde Galerie de 'L'Effort moderne' run by Léonce Rosenberg in Paris – a gallery which was dedicated to the promotion of the values of the 'call to order' movement after the end of the First World War. This painting bears an old Rosenberg stock ticket. Herbin's contemporary work is generally much more strictly geometric and symmetrical than this richly allusive and organic picture. Here, indeed, his affinities seem to be with the prewar, proto-Surrealist paintings of Duchamp and Picabia, rather than with the ordered and rational canvases of such close associates of his as Léger and Gris, while the forms themselves and the whole composition strangely anticipate the work of Surrealists of the 1930s, such as Seligmann (compare no. 71).

29

33. Aus der Sammlung: Aus einem ethnographischen Museum *(From the collection: from an ethnographical museum)* *1929* *Cut papers, photographs and gouache on paper, 26 × 17.5 Inscribed 'H. H. 29,' b.r., and 'Aus der Sammlung: Aus einem ethnographischen Museum/H. Höch 1929' on label on back*

One of the leading members of the Berlin Dada group, Höch was a brilliant exponent of the photomontage technique, which she began to use in 1918. The first works in the series *Aus einem ethnographischen Museum*, to which this belongs, date from 1925: all of them include photographs of tribal sculpture. Like the Surrealists later, the Dadaists greatly admired the art and culture of 'primitive' peoples, occasionally including masks and carvings in their own exhibitions or reproducing them in their periodicals. The mask in this collage is an ivory pendant mask from the court of Benin, Nigeria. It appears to have been cut from a photograph of a well-known mask of this type in the collection of the British Museum.

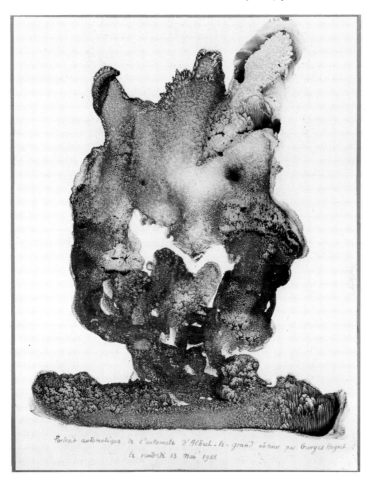

Portrait automatique de l'automate d'Albert-le-grand obtenu par Georges Hugnet le vendredi 13 Mai 1938

34. Portrait automatique de l'automate d'Albert-le-Grand *(Automatic portrait of the automaton of Albertus Magnus)* *1938*
Ink on paper, 38 × 29
Inscribed 'Portrait automatique de l'automate d'Albert-le-Grand obtenu par Georges Hugnet/le vendredi 13 Mai 1938' *b.c.*

The technique employed here is 'decalcomania'. 'Discovered' in 1935 by the Surrealist painter and object maker Oscar Dominguez, decalcomania involves laying ink, gouache etc. on a sheet of paper, and while it is still wet, placing a second sheet on top. After pressure has been applied, sometimes several times, the top sheet is then peeled off, leaving behind a richly suggestive, spongey-textured 'image', which has thus been 'obtained' 'automatically'. Decalcomania was instantly hailed as an important addition to the Surrealist repertory of alternative techniques, and was employed by many of the leading artists and poets, notably Ernst and Hugnet himself, who frequently used it to make the endpapers of books he was binding (see nos. 116 and 118). Albertus Magnus was a thirteenth-century German philosopher, mystic and natural scientist who was much admired by the Surrealists.

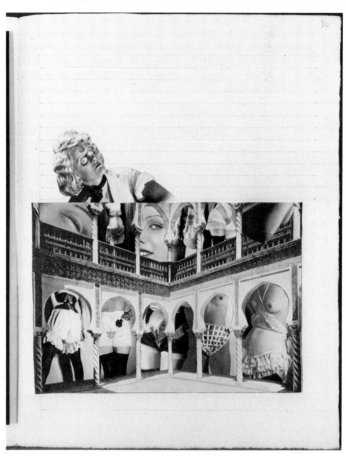

35. Untitled
date unknown
42 collages mounted in
loose gatherings;
p. 1: 32.5 × 49;
pp. 2–42: 32.5 × 24.5 each
Not inscribed

Hugnet was an important figure in the Surrealist movement during the 1930s, and in later years became one of its most enlightening first-hand witnesses. A poet and critic himself, he was also a passionate bibliophile: many of the most important books in the present collection came from his library. In 1934 he opened a bookbinding shop in Paris where he created some remarkable and unique book-covers for his Surrealist friends, incorporating elements which evoked the spirit of the text within. Given the special designation *livres-objets* (book-objects), some of these were exhibited in the *Exposition Surréaliste d'objets* in 1936, and reproduced the following year in *Minotaure* no. 10. Hugnet's devotion to craftsmanship was particularly appreciated by Duchamp, with whom he formed a close association (see no. 19). Hugnet was also active as a maker of collages. The present set of 42 has been ordered by him into a semi-narrative sequence, and the lines ruled on many of the pages appear to have been prepared to receive a text. Intended as a kind of 'collage novel', in the tradition of those created by

Ernst (see nos. 104–106), the sequence opens with a double-page spread which establishes immediately the erotic story-line and the Bluebeard-style 'medieval' castle/dungeon setting against which the subsequent sado-masochistic adventures of the heroines unfold. At page 6, interior scenes of crypts, cloisters, courtyards etc. replace the exterior castle views, and on page 16 these in turn give way to specifically ecclesiastical settings. After a brief interlude outdoors again (pages 19–21), the courtyard, gallery and bedroom scenarios return, the effect becoming ever more bordello-like. The final four images mark a return to the kinds of exterior views of castles with which the 'novel' had opened. Throughout, Hugnet has culled his imagery from a variety of sources each of which has a quite distinct style and period flavour. These include nineteenth-century engravings, turn-of-the-century picture postcards, twentieth-century advertisements, illustrations from guidebooks, photographs of movie stars and photographs from fashion journals and pornographic magazines (the latter apparently dating from the 1950s or early 1960s).

WASSILY KANDINSKY 1866–1944

36. Kleine Welten
(Small worlds)
1922, plate X
Drypoint, 28 × 22
Inscribed 'Kandinsky' *b.r.*

Kleine Welten consists of twelve woodcuts, lithographs and drypoints, some printed in colour. It was Kandinsky's most important graphic publication during his period at the Weimar Bauhaus, and dates from the time when his fully geometric, abstract style was developing out of the more painterly abstraction of the war years. This impression of plate x is from the de luxe edition of thirty out of a total edition of 230. (For full details, see H. R. Roethel, *Kandinsky. Das graphische Werk*, Cologne, DuMont Schauberg, 1970, no. 173.)

RICHARD LINDNER 1901–78

37. Solitary III *1959–62*
Oil on canvas, 106.5 × 68.5
Inscribed 'R. LINDNER/1962/
59' *b.r., and* 'R. LINDNER/
1959' *on back of canvas*

38. Untitled *1965*
Collage, 40 × 30
Inscribed 'R. LINDNER 1965'
b.r.

Born in Hamburg of an American mother, Lindner studied art in Munich in 1925–27 before settling in Paris in 1933. Interned in 1939, he eventually moved in 1941 to America, where he worked initially as an illustrator for such magazines as *Vogue* and *Harper's Bazaar*. It was only in the 1950s that he was able to devote himself to painting. Lindner's experience of the art world in Germany and France as well as in America helps to explain the connections between his work and that of such artists as Duchamp, Picabia, Schlemmer and especially Bellmer.

39. Le miroir magique
(The magic mirror)
1929
Oil on canvas, 73 × 54
Inscribed 'Magritte' *b.r.*
FRONT COVER

Not exhibited until 1933, when it was included in Magritte's one-man show at the Palais des Beaux-Arts in Brussels. It was painted during his three-year period of residence in the Parisian suburb of Le Perreux-sur-Marne, where he had moved in the late summer of 1927 in order to be in closer contact with the French Surrealist group. Magritte had been represented in a Surrealist exhibition in the Galerie Goemans in Paris in 1928, but his work was not featured in *La Révolution Surréaliste* until the final issue, dated 15 December 1929. There, however, his new-found prominence within the official group around Breton – during the period of deep crisis and realignment that saw the expulsion of such leading figures as Robert Desnos and André Masson – was fully acknowledged. His photomontage of one of his recent canvases, *The hidden woman*, surrounded by photographs of himself and the remaining members of the group, was given pride of place as the final image in the whole review; and his important text, 'Les mots et les images', was published. This text, which consists of a series of illustrated propositons investigating the relationship between words, images and things, is particularly relevant to *Le miroir magique*, itself a fine example of the long series of word paintings which Magritte had inaugurated soon after he settled in France.

40. La gâcheuse
(The bungler) 1935
Gouache on paper, 20 × 13.5
Inscribed 'Magritte' *t.r.*
ILLUSTRATED ON P. 72

This was chosen for the cover of the Belgian edition of the *Bulletin International du Surréalisme*, dated 20 August 1935.

41. La représentation
(The representation)
1937
Oil on canvas mounted on panel, 48.5 × 44
Inscribed 'Magritte' *b.l.*
ILLUSTRATED OPPOSITE

First exhibited in December 1937 in a three-man show with Tanguy and Man Ray at the Palais des Beaux-Arts in Brussels, it was formerly in the collections of Paul Eluard and Roland Penrose. The only shaped canvas in Magritte's œuvre, it was cut down from a conventional rectangular format and a special frame was made for it. It may be seen as a development from *Eternal evidence*, 1930, which represents a full-length standing female nude by means of five small, rectangular framed portions (head, breasts, pubic area, knees, and ankles), and from other erotic paintings of the early 1930s, which include a framed female torso. The most provocative of these was the notorious female face-torso called *The rape*, a drawing of which appeared on the cover of Breton's *Qu'est-ce que le surréalisme?* in 1934.

(no. 41)

JOAN MIRÓ 1893–1983

42. Peinture *(Painting)*
1927
Oil on canvas, 33 × 24
Inscribed 'Miró' *b.r., and*
'Joan Miró/1927' *on back*
of canvas

This is no. 221 in J. Dupin, *Joan Miró. Life and work*, New York, 1961. Although on a diminutive scale, it is very characteristic of the works Miró executed in Paris during the period 1925–27, when he was working with great freedom and rapidity in response to the stimulus of surrealist poetry and of his own, apparently hallucinated, visions. These paintings have a highly abstracted, calligraphic appearance, but all of them have some vestigial figurative content, and it was at this period that Miró began to develop the primitivistic 'sign language' which was to be intrinsic to his work for the rest of his career. Thus the large dot radiating lines at the top right-hand side of this picture, and the pin-man figure below it, appear in many other contemporary works.

EDUARDO PAOLOZZI born 1924

43. Three men in
a boat *1946*
Pen and ink and wash on
paper, 47.5 × 57
Inscribed 'Eduardo Paolozzi
1946' *b.r.*

One of a series of ink drawings of fishermen executed in 1946 which reveal Paolozzi's keen interest in African sculpture, and in the graphic style of earlier European masters such as Picasso and Klee who had themselves been influenced by tribal art.

44. [Head] *1946*
Ink and coloured papers on
paper, 37.5 × 28
Inscribed 'June 1946' *c.*

After studying at Edinburgh College of Art, Paolozzi went to the Slade School of Art in 1945. In London he spent more time in the museums and galleries and browsing through magazines and manuals of machines etc. than in the Slade studios. Favourite

45. [Head] *1946*
Ink and coloured papers on paper, 49 × 23.5
Inscribed 'Eduardo Paolozzi 1946' *b.r.*

46. [Man and woman] *c. 1947*
Ink and coloured papers on paper, 29 × 22
Not inscribed

47. [Oil lamp] *1947*
Coloured papers and gouache on paper, 48 × 22.5
Inscribed 'April, 1947' *b.l., and* 'E. Paolozzi' *b.r.*

48. [Head] *1947*
Ink, gouache and collage on paper, 24 × 18.5
Inscribed 'April 1947' *b.l., and* 'E. Paolozzi' *b.r.*
COLOUR PLATE

49. Shooting gallery *1947*
Ink, gouache, charcoal and collage on paper, 26.5 × 35
Inscribed 'Eduardo Paolozzi' *c., and* 'August 1947' *b.r.*

50. Fair drawing *1947*
Ink and gouache on paper, 28 × 31
Inscribed 'November. Eduardo Paolozzi. 47.' *b.r.*

51. [Booth] *1947*
Ink, gouache and collage on paper, 25.5 × 32
Inscribed 'E. Paolozzi' *b.r.*

52. London zoo aquirium *1951*
Ink and watercolour on paper, 56 × 76
Inscribed 'LONDON ZOO AQUIRIUM E PAOLOZZI 1951', *b.c. to b.r.*

53. Aquarium *1951*
Lithograph heightened with gouache, 55 × 58
Inscribed 'AQUARIUM E. PAOLOZZI 1951', *b.c. to b.r.*

haunts included the Natural History and the Science Museums in South Kensington and the ethnographical collections in the British Museum. He had his first one-man exhibition at the Mayor Gallery in London in January 1947. That summer he went to Paris, where he pursued this search for visual and intellectual stimuli and became fascinated by Dada and Surrealism and by Dubuffet's concept and collection of *Art Brut*. In Paris his knowledge of the work of Picasso, Miró, Ernst, Klee and Giacometti deepened, and their influence is often apparent in his work of the late 1940s. This group of drawings and collages was executed while Paolozzi was a student in London and during his first months in Paris. The gouaches of street booths and fairground shooting galleries were among the first works he made in Paris and reflect his response to the rich street life of the city.

Paolozzi returned to London in 1949 and began teaching textile design at the Central School of Arts and Crafts – the first of several posts at art colleges in England and abroad. His continuing fascination with natural history and his sympathy with the contemporary work of Dubuffet and the concept of *Art Brut* are apparent in these two works. Contemporary with them, and related to them in the jagged quality and the intricate play of the line, were two public-scale sculptures Paolozzi designed for the Festival of Britain: *The cage*, an aptly named openwork, freestanding structure resembling twisted wire, and *Fountain*, a monumental 'space cage'.

37

54. Collage *1953*
Coloured paper, silkscreen,
ink, watercolour, and gouache
on paper, 53 × 69
Inscribed 'Eduardo Paolozzi
1953.' *b.c.*

Paolozzi's admiration for the collages of Schwitters is evident in this work, which creates a similarly paradoxical balance between controlled structure and found 'rubbish', between formal abstraction and resonant memorials of lived experiences. (Compare no. 70.) In preparing it Paolozzi made screenprinted sheets which he then tore up into irregular pieces, rearranging them later into a loosely rectilinear order suggestive of an architectural plan or an aerial view. In conversation with Edouard Roditi (*Arts*, May 1959) he remarked: 'I suppose I am interested, above all, in investigating the golden ability of the artist to achieve a metamorphosis of quite ordinary things into something wonderful and extraordinary that is neither nonsensical nor morally edifying.'

55. Head and arm
c. 1954
Bronze, h. 14

56. Head *1955*
Pen and ink on paper,
34 × 26
Inscribed 'E. Paolozzi
August 9th' *b.l., and* '1955'
b.r.

These two works are typical of the many representations of the human head which Paolozzi made in the mid-1950s. Their rough, expressive surfaces and deliberately primitive aspect, and the touch of grotesque humour they exude, are further indication of his continuing interest in the work of Klee and especially Dubuffet. In common with these artists, Paolozzi uses complex graphic detailing to suggest an active inner life.

57. [Figure] *1957*
Bronze, 107 × 23.5 × 13
Inscribed 'E. PAOLOZZI.
AUG. 1957' *on base*

58. [Man with arms
raised] *1958*
Bronze, h. 25
Inscribed 'E. PAOLOZZI
1958' *on base*

In these works Paolozzi adapts the collage process to the making of sculpture, creating richly suggestive and fantastic effects through the accumulation of found objects which have been embedded in the surfaces through casting. The aim is to achieve an effect of metamorphosis, to multiply the possible references and meanings so that the identity of the figure is in a constant state of flux.

59. Metallization of a
dream *1963*
Screenprint on paper, 53 × 48
Not inscribed

This was derived from a collage of the same title executed in 1962.

60. Tafel 16 *1964*
Collage on paper, 64.5 × 30
Inscribed 'TAFEL 16' *b.l., and* 'EDUARDO PAOLOZZI 1964' *b.r.*

(no. 61)

61. Untitled *1951–63*
Collages on paper,
various dimensions

A group of eighteen unpublished collages dated between 1951 and 1963.

EDUARDO PAOLOZZI and R. B. KITAJ born 1932

62. Work in progress
1962
Framed collage, 85 × 100
ILLUSTRATED OVERLEAF

In 1952, Paolozzi was (with Richard Hamilton and Lawrence Alloway) one of the founder members of the Independent Group. Among the subjects discussed at meetings held in the Institute of Contemporary Arts were the relevance for art of recent developments in science and technology, the mass media and popular culture – concerns which lie at the heart of British Pop art in the later 1950s and the 1960s, and of the work of Paolozzi himself at that period. (The 'lecture' he gave at the first meeting at the ICA, when he projected numerous images of advertisements, comics, film stills etc. in random order and with no verbal commentary, has come to be regarded as a landmark in the prehistory of British Pop.) *Work in progress* reflects precisely these kinds of interests, and relates quite closely to the contemporary work of Peter Blake. It was one of two collaborations with Kitaj, who had studied art in New York and

39

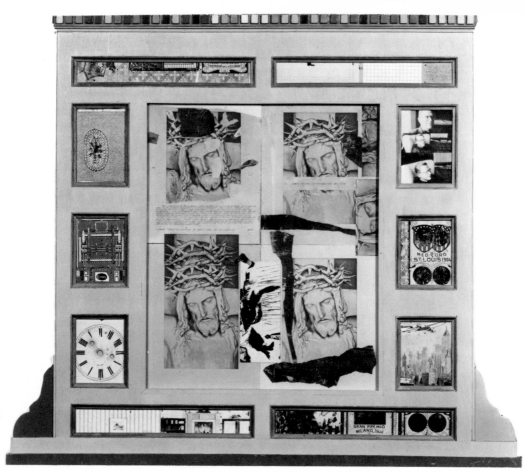

Vienna before moving to England to continue first in Oxford, and then at the Royal College of Art in London (1960–62). Kitaj, whose culture was exceptionally broadly based, sympathised fully with Paolozzi's extra-artistic interests, and shared his fascination with ready-made visual material and collage techniques. The great density of reference and association in this work, which must be read as well as looked at, and which in that respect is the direct heir to the Duchampian tradition, is perhaps even more typical of Kitaj than of Paolozzi.

ROLAND PENROSE 1900–1984

63. Untitled *1937*
Collage and pencil on
millboard, 78.5 × 54
Inscribed 'R. Penrose. 37' b.r.

Penrose first went to Paris in 1922, and by the early 1930s had become close friends with leading members in the Surrealist group, notably Ernst and Man Ray. In 1930 he had a walk-on part in *L'Age d'or*, the second Surrealist film made by Buñuel and Dalí, and in 1934 he organised the publication of Ernst's latest collage novel, *Une Semaine de bonté* (no. 106). Back in England in 1935, he masterminded the International Surrealist exhibition held at the New Burlington Galleries in London the following year. In 1937 he and E. L. T. Mesens took over the London Gallery, which was henceforth to be largely dedicated to the promotion of Surrealist art, and in the following year he helped launch *London Bulletin* (no. 161). It was in *London Bulletin* in 1939 (no. 17, 'Colour-colours, or an experiment by Roland Penrose') that Magritte and Paul Nougé published their article on his series of collages made from postcards collected in the South of France. They described his innovation in works like the one shown here thus: 'Roland Penrose has thought of formulating the problem [of colour] in entirely new terms: up till now, he says, colour has been used for no other purpose than the creation of the image of objects. *But what if we tried to use the image of the objects to create colours?*'

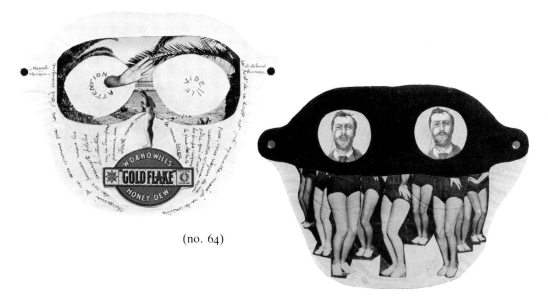

(no. 64)

64. Attention le vide!! *(Beware the void!!) 1938*
Collage on paper, 15 × 20
Inscribed 'ATTENTION LE VIDE!!' *within lenses, and* 'à Marcel/Mariën' *t.l., and* 'de Roland/Penrose' *t.r.*

Penrose made this collage-mask for Marcel Mariën, whom at the time he knew only 'par l'œil unique/de vos poèmes mais les/escargots fideles/de intuition,/ ne se trempent/jamais [*sic*]' (by the unique eye of your poems, but the faithful snails of intuition are never wrong). Mariën has confirmed the date as 1938. The two images of a bespectacled man collaged in the lenses on the back of the mask have been cut from the image entitled 'VIVE LA FRANCE (au phonoscope)' which appears as an ironic illustration to 'La prière du soldat', an anti-militaristic text published in the final issue of *La Révolution Surréaliste*, December 1929 (p. 21). Mariën was himself a prolific maker of collages and objects as well as being a poet and critic. He joined the Brussels Surrealist group in 1937, when he was seventeen years old, and quickly became one of the most active members, contributing to the Surrealist section of the exhibition *Young Belgian Painters*, organised at the London Galley in 1937, writing regularly for Surrealist reviews in the 1940s and thereafter, and generally encouraging a strongly 'interventionist' and 'political' stance within the movement as a whole. In recent years he has published all the most important documents relating to the Surrealist movement in Belgium from its earliest beginnings in the 1920s.

FRANCIS PICABIA 1879–1953

65. Fille née sans mère *(Girl born without a mother) 1916–17*
Gouache and metallic paint on paper, 50 × 65
Inscribed 'FILLE NÉE SANS MÈRE' *b.l., and* 'BARCELONE Picabia' *b.r.*
Erased inscription 'CETTE MACHINE A LE POUVOIR' *t.c.*
COLOUR PLATE

As for many of his machine paintings of the wartime years, Picabia has cannibalised a diagram from a technical journal for this work. In May 1915 he arrived in New York and immediately joined the proto-Dadaist circle of avant-garde artists, which was supported by Walter Arensberg and included, among others, Duchamp and Man Ray. He collaborated on *291* (see no. 175), publishing there his first machine works, including a drawing also called *Fille née sans mère* (no. 4, June 1915). This title, like many others Picabia gave to his machine works, is an ironic adaptation from the pages of 'Locutions latines et étrangères' (Latin and foreign phrases) published on pink paper in the centre of the *Petit Larousse illustré* (Paris, 1914 etc.). The phrase in question is 'Prolem sine matre creatam', which is translated as 'Enfant né sans mère' (child born without a mother), and defined as '. . . an epigraph taken from Ovid's *Metamorphoses* which Montesquieu placed at the beginning of his *Esprit des lois* to signify that he had had no model for it'. *Fille née sans mère* relates closely to more explicitly sexual machine images Picabia executed in 1916–18, such as *Machine turn quickly* and *Amorous parade*, to others with obvious religious references, such as *The Holy Virgin* (represented by an ink blot), and to Duchamp's work on *The large glass* (1915–23).

66. Sotileza *(Subtlety)*
c. 1928
Gouache, watercolour and chalk on paper, 74 × 53.5
Inscribed 'Francis Picabia' *b.l. and* 'Sotileza/Nicanor Villalta' *c.*
ILLUSTRATED OPPOSITE

In 1927–28 Picabia embarked on a new style which he practised with increasing complexity for a few years. In these 'Transparencies' successive layers of images are superimposed upon one another in a way which enables Picabia both to explore complex spatial effects without resorting to conventional perspectival systems, and to oppose and contrast antithetical styles of painting and drawing. In this work, as in several others painted after his return trip to Spain in the summer of 1927, Picabia contrasts the kitschy, idealised 'naturalism' used for the Spanish lady in her lace mantilla with the severely abstracted style of Catalan Romanesque art used for the Madonna figure outlined on top.

(no. 66)

PABLO PICASSO 1881–1973

67. Mort de Marat
(Death of Marat) 1934
Coloured drypoint on paper,
13.5 × 10.5
Not inscribed

This relates closely to an earlier painting now in the Musée Picasso in Paris, *Woman with a stiletto (Death of Marat)*, 1931. Dated 21 July 1934, this was made for Benjamin Péret's *De derrière les fagots*, Paris, Editions Surréalistes, 1934. There were three states preceding the state used for the book. Picasso pulled four impressions of the third state in red, green and blue: this is one of those. On the same copperplate, on 22 September 1934, he engraved a different composition, *Minotaure aveuglé guidé par une fillette, I.* The whole plate, with the *Mort de Marat* composition crossed through, was published by Vollard in 1939. (For full details, see B. Geiser, *Picasso. Peintre-Graveur*, Vol. II, *Catalogue raisonné de l'œuvre gravé et des monotypes, 1932–34*, Berne, 1968, no. 430.)

MAN RAY 1890–1976

68. [Studio door] *1939?*
Oil on canvas, 65 × 49.5
Inscribed 'Man Ray' *b.l.*
COLOUR PLATE

The date of 1939 has been suggested for this relatively little-known work because '39' appears twice among the lists of numbers inscribed on the door and the satchel – a device for concealing/revealing a date which Man Ray used on other occasions. Known best perhaps for his superb and technically innovative photographs, Man Ray had been prolific as both a painter and a maker of objects since his Dada years with Duchamp in New York during the First World War. Like Picabia, another close friend and fellow iconoclast, with whom Man Ray shared a profound contempt for consistency, his style as a painter was subject to unpredictable shifts and turns. The ironic suggestions of casual graffiti in this picture recall such important Picabias as *L'œil cacodylate*, 1921, which is composed almost entirely of inscriptions.

OSKAR SCHLEMMER 1888–1943

69. Kopf nach links, mit schwarzer Kontur
(Head in profile with black contour line)
1920–21
Lithograph, 25 × 20
Inscribed 'Oskar Schlemmer' *b.r.*

This is one of some twenty lithographs Schlemmer executed between 1913 and 1928. It was published in the portfolio *Die Schaffenden*, Weimar, Euphorion-Verlag, 1921, and is identical to a pen and ink drawing of the same date. (See W. Grohmann, *Oskar Schlemmer. Zeichnungen und Graphik. Œuvrekatalog*, Stuttgart, 1965, no. GL6.) Schlemmer was a master at the Bauhaus from 1920–28, directing the stonemasonry and metal workshops, and, at Dessau, the stage workshop. His *Triadic ballet* was first performed at Stuttgart in 1922. The style of this head is typical of his stage designs.

70. Mz. 299 *1921*
Collage on paper,
20 × 16 including mount
*Inscribed '*Mz. 299/für
V. I. Kuron' *b.l., and*
'Kurt Schwitters. 1921.'
b.r.

Schwitters's first collages date from 1918, the year in which he met Arp, Hausmann and other members of the German Dada movement. In the following year, some were exhibited in the Der Sturm gallery in Berlin. Schwitters remained closely allied with the various Dada groups in Germany, but his own movement, which he called *Merz* and which he ran from Hanover, was distinct from Dada in his insistence that his work was to be understood as art, not as the negation of art. This attitude irritated several of the Dadaists, but enabled him to collaborate with other avant-garde abstractionist groups, in particular the Constructivists. In 1923 the first issue of his magazine, also called *Merz*, was published, and he began work on the construction of the first *Merzbau* (Merzhouse) in Hanover – an extension of his collage methods into an environmental dimension. *Mz. 299* employs a favourite structural device of Schwitters – cutting diagonals which intersect towards the bottom at a central vertical axis to produce the effect of a controlled 'explosion'.

KURT SELIGMANN 1901–62

71. Le parachutiste
(The parachutist) 1934
Etching on paper, 34 × 26
Inscribed 'LA
PARACHÛTISTE' t.r.,
'Kurt Seligmann' b.l.,
and 'Le Parachutiste' b.r.

This plate was published in an edition of 100 as an illustration to Pierre Courthion's *Les Vagabondes héraldiques*, Paris, 1934. Born in Basel, Seligmann moved to Paris in the 1920s, and in 1930 he joined the *Abstraction-Création* group. Soon, however, he was moving in Surrealist circles, and his *Ultra-furniture* – a pseudo-Baroque stool mounted on women's high-heeled legs – was a *succès de scandale* at the International Surrealist exhibition held in Paris in 1938. With several other leading members of the Surrealist group, he moved to New York during the Second World War, where he was a regular contributor to *VVV* and *View* (see nos. 177 and 178).

YVES TANGUY 1900–1955

72. Le ruban des excès
(The ribbon of excess)
1932
Oil on panel, 35 × 45
Inscribed 'YVES TANGUY 32' b.r., and 'Le Ruban des Excès/
YVES TANGUY 1932' on back of panel
COLOUR PLATE

This work was formerly in the collection of Roland Penrose.

73. Jamais plus
(Never more) 1939
Oil on canvas, 92 × 73
Inscribed 'YVES TANGUY 39'
b.r.

Like *Le ruban des excès* this is an excellent example of Tanguy's highly refined and meticulous style of the 1930s, in which abstract biomorphic forms as three-dimensional in effect as tiny sculptures are presented in a deep illusionistic space. In the alliance between the sense of an entirely private dream- or fantasy-world and of tangible 'reality', we find the realisation of the ultimate Surrealist goal, which Breton defined as the 'reconciliation of opposites'. Tanguy joined the Surrealist group in 1925, having decided to become a painter after seeing de Chirico's *Child's brain* in the window of a dealer's gallery in Paris. The naivety of his earliest pictures was greatly appreciated by Breton, and from 1926 onwards his work was reproduced in *La Révolution Surréaliste*. In 1927 Breton wrote the preface to his exhibition at the Galerie Surréaliste in Paris – an indication of his particular sympathy with Tanguy's vision. Unlike many of the other painters in the movement, who eventually found Breton intolerably autocratic, Tanguy remained devoted to him for the rest of his life.

YVES TANGUY, with ANDRÉ BRETON and JACQUELINE BRETON

74. Cadavre exquis
(Exquisite corpse) 1938
Collage on paper, 29.5 × 20

The *cadavre exquis*, whether visual or verbal, was a favourite game with the Surrealists, and several *cadavres exquis* were reproduced in *La Révolution Surréaliste* nos. 9–10, October 1927. A collaboration involving usually three or four people, it is in essence identical to the children's game of 'Consequences' in which the participants complete a sentence or a drawing of a figure without seeing what has been done already. The name the Surrealists gave to the game was derived from a sentence that had been produced collaboratively in this way: 'Le cadavre exquis boira le vin nouveau' (The exquisite corpse will drink the new wine). The example displayed here was made using cut-outs from nineteenth-century magazines during the weekend of 7–9 February 1938, when André and Jacqueline Breton and Yves and Jeannette Tanguy were staying with Charles Ratton and his wife at Saint-Queux. (Ratton was a dealer in primitive art, and a close friend of the Surrealists. His gallery in Paris was the venue for the famous *Exposition Surréaliste d'objets* in May 1936.)

WILLIAM TURNBULL born 1922

75. Metamorphosis I
1980
Bronze, h. 33
Inscribed '80 Ⓣ 1/9'

This was first exhibited in Turnbull's one-man show at the Waddington Galleries in London in March 1981. As a student at the Slade (1946–48) Turnbull met Paolozzi, and together they went to Paris in 1947, where they visited the Musée de l'Homme and Dubuffet's *Foyer de l'Art Brut*. Turnbull's continuing interest in non-European cultures and in the sacred character of their art is reflected in this work, which bears some resemblance to prehistoric Cycladic figurines in its shape and form, and appears to allude to 'primitive' ritualistic usages of art in the marks pierced on the surface.

LAURENCE VAIL 1891–1968

76. Seascape *1943*
Collage on wine bottle, with painted wooden stopper, h. 35
Not inscribed

Vail was never an official member of the Surrealist movement but, through his relationship with Peggy Guggenheim, was well acquainted with the Surrealists in New York during the Second World War. In the 1930s Magritte had made frequent use of wine bottles as a support, but for painting not for collage. The effect of *Seascape*, with its obsessive accretion of collaged elements, is reminiscent of Victorian-period scrapbooks and screens – precisely the kinds of popular/folk art so much appreciated by the Surrealists. An elaborate nineteenth-century scrap-covered screen had, indeed, been reproduced full-page in the seventh issue of *La Révolution Surréaliste*, June 1926 (p. 13).

ANDY WARHOL 1930–87

77. Portrait of Maurice
1976
Oil and silkscreen on canvas, 65.5 × 81
Inscribed 'Andy Warhol 76' on back edge of canvas

The subject is the collector's pet dog, now deceased. The painting was obtained from Warhol in exchange for a set of his silkscreen prints of Marilyn Monroe (1967).

Francis BACON, *Figure study I* (no. 2)

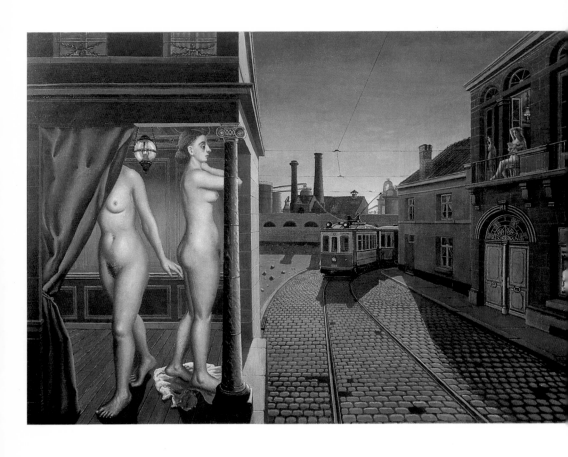

Paul DELVAUX, *La rue du tramway* (no. 16)

Marcel DUCHAMP, *Boîte-en-valise* (no. 19)

Max ERNST, *Max Ernst montrant à une jeune fille la tête de son père* (no. 25)

opposite above Alberto GIACOMETTI, *Objet désagréable à jeter* (no. 29)

opposite below Eduardo PAOLOZZI, [*Head*] (no. 48)

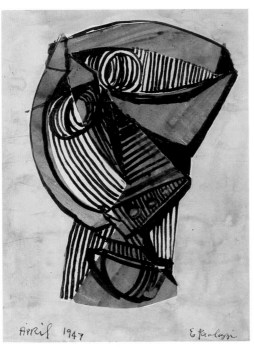

April 1947   E. Paolozzi

Francis PICABIA, *Fille née sans mère* (no. 65)

Man RAY, [*Studio door*] (no. 68)

Yves TANGUY, *Le ruban des excès* (no. 72)

Photographs

DORA MAAR

78. Portrait de Georges Hugnet *1934*
23 × 17.7
Inscribed 'Dora Maar' b.r.

Dora Maar participated briefly in the Surrealist movement during the mid-1930s as a photographer. In 1935 Eluard introduced her to Picasso, and she became his companion for several years, inspiring many important paintings (including *The weeping woman*, 1937), and for a time virtually supplanting Brassaï as the unofficial photographer of his work. She photographed the successive states of *Guernica* and collaborated with Picasso on a series of photographic etchings (published in *Cahiers d'Art* in 1937).

MAN RAY

79. Portrait de Georges Hugnet *1934*
23 × 17.5
Inscribed 'Man Ray' b.r.

This photo-portrait was used in *Surrealist Chessboard*, Man Ray's montage of members of the Surrealist group made in 1934.

80. Gisèle Prassinos reading her poems to the Surrealists *1934*
17.5 × 22.5
Inscribed 'Man Ray Paris' b.r.

Gisèle Prassinos, the child prodigy espoused by the Surrealists (see no. 3), is reading her poems to: (seated l. to r.) André Breton and Paul Eluard; (standing l. to r.) Mario Prassinos, Henri Parisot, Benjamin Péret and René Char. Mario Prassinos, Gisèle's older brother, had discovered her poems, which, according to her, were written purely 'automatically' and quite without knowledge of modern poetry or Surrealism. He showed them to Henri Parisot, who, recognising their surreal quality, took them to Breton and Eluard. A reading was immediately organised. All doubts as to the authenticity of the poems banished, a session in Man Ray's studio was arranged, and this photograph was the result. From then onwards Gisèle was an occasional, if somewhat bemused, participant at Surrealist gatherings at the Café de la Place Blanche. Her 'Contes et poèmes', and a photo-portrait by Man Ray, were published in *Minotaure* no. 6, winter 1934–35.

MAN RAY with TRISTAN TZARA

81. Tristan Tzara and Jean Cocteau *c. 1923*
8.5 × 6
Not inscribed, but bearing Man Ray's studio stamp

The photograph has been 'embellished' in black ink by Tzara.

Books and Manuscripts

LOUIS ARAGON

82. Le Con d'Irène
Paris, published clandestinely,
1928
With five original etchings by André Masson
24.5 × 19.5
No. 127 out of a total edition of 150

Neither author nor artist is identified.

HANS BELLMER

83. Die Puppe
Karlsruhe, privately printed,
1934
12 × 9

Copy dedicated to Guy Lévis-Mano, who published the French edition. It consists of a series of ten photographs of Bellmer's first Doll, recording successive stages in its construction, together with a poetic text by Bellmer. The Doll was made with the help of Bellmer's brother, who was an engineer.

84. La Poupée
Paris, GLM, 1936
17 × 12.5
No. 85 out of a total edition
of 100

The French edition of *Die Puppe*. Bellmer's text was translated from the German by Robert Valançay under the title 'Souvenirs relatifs à la poupée'. Eighteen photographs of the 'articulated minor' had already been published in *Minotaure* no. 6, winter 1934–35.

85. Les Jeux de la Poupée

Typescript of Bellmer's text for the above publication, and manuscript of Georges Hugnet's translation of the text, together with original pencil and gouache drawing by Bellmer

1938–39

Les Jeux de la Poupée was eventually published in 1949 (Paris, Editions Premières), but was prepared for publication a decade earlier. The publishing house was to have been Editions des Cahiers d'Art, but the outbreak of war made the realisation of the project impossible. The book includes fifteen tinted photographs of Bellmer's second Doll, 'illustrated' with prose poems by Paul Eluard inspired by the Doll. In addition there is a long introductory text by Bellmer, translated into French by Hugnet. The manuscript exhibited here is Hugnet's draft translation, with numerous corrections by Bellmer. Also exhibited is the typescript – on pink paper – of Bellmer's text in German. The draft design of the prospectus for the projected publication in 1939 (also exhibited) reveals that the title was originally to have been 'Jeux vagues de la Poupée'. It is decorated with Bellmer's designs for the illustration. The prospectus itself indicates that a total edition of 356 copies was envisaged by Editions des Cahiers d'Art.

ANDRÉ BRETON

86. Le Révolver à cheveux blancs

Paris, Editions des Cahiers Libres, 1932
With frontispiece etching by Salvador Dalí
20 × 15.5
No. 10 out of a total edition of 1010
Inscribed 'André Breton'

This copy was in the collection of Georges Hugnet. It contains an original drawing by Dalí of himself with Gala. It also contains Breton's manuscript of 'Façon', the first poem in the anthology.

87. Yves Tanguy
New York, Pierre Matisse Editions, 1946
No. 234 out of a total edition of 1150

With an original drawing by Tanguy on the title-page.

ANDRÉ BRETON and SALVADOR DALÍ

88. Manuscript letters and postcards
1930–39

A collection of fourteen letters and postcards between Breton and Dalí. The earliest item is a postcard from Dalí postmarked 11 March 1930; the latest is a letter from Breton dated 6 January 1939. The correspondence as a whole documents Breton's ultimately unsuccessful efforts to make Dalí conform to Surrealist orthodoxy and to contribute regularly to the activities and publications of the official Surrealist group, and Dalí's protestations of 'unconditional' adherence to Surrealism, but defence of his right to express himself verbally or in his writings and paintings as he feels personally compelled to. In particular, a group of very important letters dating from 1933–34 reflects

Breton's severe anxiety over such issues as Dalí's seemingly ambivalent attitude to Lenin, stated fascination with Hitler, and reported admiration for academic art and hostility to modern art. In one of these letters, dated 3 February 1934, Breton informs Dalí that the decision has been taken at a 'general assembly' of the Surrealists to exclude him from the group because he has been found 'guilty of counter-revolutionary acts tending to the glorification of Hitlerian fascism'. This decision was revoked, and friendly relations were re-established, after Dalí offered a detailed explanation of his motivation and behaviour (undated letter from Dalí in two versions, one in his own hand, the other largely in Gala Dalí's hand). Other subjects raised in Breton's letters include the need for coherent and uniform group action on all fronts, plans for new issues of *Minotaure* and for major Surrealist exhibitions in Paris and Tenerife, and accounts of the 'considerable success' of Breton's and Eluard's lecture tour to Prague in 1935.

ANDRÉ BRETON and PAUL ÉLUARD

89. L'Immaculée conception
Paris, Editions Surréalistes, 1930
With a frontispiece by Salvador Dalí
23.5 × 18.8
No. 1646 out of a total edition of 2111

The texts, simulating as closely as possible the delirium of the insane, were written collaboratively by Breton and Eluard. Dalí's parallel identification with insanity is expressed in the theory of the 'Paranoiac-critical method' which he developed, and first put into practice in his paintings, in 1929–30 (see no. 11).

JEAN-PAUL COLLET

90. Flaques; poèmes
Paris, Les Ecrivains Réunis, 1935
With three original aquatints by Kurt Seligmann
28 × 21.5
No. 55 out of a total edition of 140

RENÉ CREVEL

91. Mr Knife and Miss Fork
Translated by Kay Boyle
Paris, The Black Sun Press, 1931
With nineteen photograms of frottages by Max Ernst
18.5 × 12
No. 12 out of a total edition of 255

The binding was also designed by Ernst. The text is described as 'a fragment of the novel Babylone'.

92. La Femme visible
Paris, Editions Surréalistes,
1930
With frontispiece etching
by Dalí
28 × 22
No. 121 out of a total edition
of 204

The cover has a close-up photograph of the eyes of Gala, whom Dalí had met for the first time in the summer of 1929 when she and Eluard came to visit him in Cadaquès. From that time onwards they were inseparable. *La Femme visible* contains a number of Dalí's published writings, including 'L'Ane pourri', where he outlines his theory of the 'Paranoiac-critical method'.

(no. 93)

93. Manuscript with illustrations of the scenario of a projected 'Documentary film' on Surrealism
c. 1931
Thirteen pages of text, plus
three photographs (including
Man Ray's Indestructible
object*)*
33 × 24
Inscribed 'Salvador Dalí'

Formerly in the collection of Georges Hugnet. Dalí describes this scenario as a 'sketch of the essential ideas' for the 'argument' of the film. It is, he says, to be made with the collaboration of the Surrealists (first page of ms.). The scenes planned included definitions of Surrealism ('Surrealism can be practised by everyone', etc.), demonstrations of automatic writing and the creation of *cadavres exquis*, a discourse on Freud and his concepts of the unconscious and the pleasure principle, and an account of Dalí's 'Paranoiac-critical method'. The final oration was to be delivered by Breton. Dalí's fascination with the cinema was life-long, although some of his cinematic projects – including this one – came to nothing. In the spring of 1929 he had written the scenario for *Un Chien andalou*, the first of two Surrealist films made with Luis Buñuel – the second being *L'Age d'or* (1930). In 1932 *Babaouo*, his scenario for another film which was never made, was published (Paris, Editions des Cahiers Libres). Several years later there was an abortive attempt to make a film with the Marx Brothers. But in 1944 he successfully created the dream sequence for Hitchcock's *Spellbound* (1945), and he followed this with the dream sequence for Minelli's *Father of the Bride* (1950).

94. Salvador Dalí
New York, Julien Levy Gallery, 1939
32.5 × 25.5

Formerly in the collection of Marcel Mariën. The exhibition opened on 21 March 1939 and caused an enormous stir in the American press – in part the result of a widely reported fracas a few days earlier during which Dalí, who was designing an elaborate décor for the Bonwit Teller store on Fifth Avenue, became enraged by changes that had been made without his consent, and crashed through the shop window onto the street. The exhibition sold out.

ROBERT DESNOS

95. Deuil pour deuil
Paris, Editions du Sagittaire, 1924
16 × 12
Inscribed 'à Charles Duhamel/ ce livre a Colin Maillard/Paris 4.2.24/Robert Desnos'

Desnos participated actively in the Surrealist group from 1922 onwards, and was particularly famed during the *époque des sommeils* (period of trances, 1922–24) for his ability to enter a trance-state at will and then to speak or write 'automatically'. He wrote regularly for *La Révolution Surréaliste*, but quarrelled with Breton in 1929 and left the group. (He is one of those savagely attacked by Breton in the 'Second Manifeste du Surréalisme', 1929.)

MARCEL DUCHAMP

96. La mariée mise à nu par ses célibataires, même,
known as The green box
Paris, Editions Rrose Sélavy, September 1934; 33×28×2.5
Inscribed 'Marcel Duchamp 1934' on the spine inside the box, and 'POUR HUGNET' pin-pricked through the flock lining of the back inside cover of the box
No. XIII out of the de luxe edition of XX; regular edition of 300

This copy was dedicated to Georges Hugnet. *The green box* is the essential companion piece to *The large glass*, which Duchamp had abandoned as 'definitively unfinished' in 1923. Within a green flocked cardboard box he assembled one colour plate under glass and 93 facsimiles of the preparatory notes, sketches, and photographs, dating from the years 1911–15. (Each copy of the de luxe edition contains in addition one manuscript page or an original drawing. The box of the de luxe edition has thin copper strips pasted on back and front forming the letters M and D.) The order of the notes was random, leaving the reader to create his own sequence. In preparing the facsimiles Duchamp adopted the most painstaking and meticulous methods. He scoured Paris for papers that were exactly like those used originally, and for lithographic inks which were exactly the same colour as the inks, etc. he had used. A template was made for each note – the notes had been written on irregular scraps of paper – and the facsimiles were individually torn around the template: that is, 320 times for each note. He explained to Pierre Cabanne: 'I wanted that album to go with the "Glass", and to be consulted when seeing the "Glass" because, as I see it, it must not be "looked at" in the aesthetic sense of the word. One must consult the book, and see the two together. The conjunction of the two things entirely removes the retinal aspect that I don't like' (*Dialogues with Marcel Duchamp*, London, 1971, pp. 42–43).

97. Letters from Marcel Duchamp to Georges Hugnet
Manuscripts
1941

A group of brief letters relating to the preparation of the *Boîte en valise* (see no. 19). Duchamp writes of his difficulties, and eventual success, in obtaining a pass to travel in and out of the occupied zone; he alludes to his meeting with the saddler who is supplying the skins needed to cover the valises; and he arranges meetings with Hugnet, for whom one of the valises is being prepared.

98. Lettre de Marcel Duchamp à Tristan Tzara
December 1958
Celluloid engraved by Tristan Tzara, and inscribed 'TZARA' b.r.
No. 17 out of a total edition of 25
Inscribed 'Marcel Duchamp' on back page

The letter from Duchamp dates from 1921. A very rare item, this copy was dedicated to Hugnet by Duchamp in 1961.

PAUL ÉLUARD

99. Les Malheurs des immortels: révélés par Paul Eluard et Max Ernst
Paris, Librairie Six, 1922
With reproductions of twenty-one collages by Max Ernst
25 × 19

Eluard has dedicated this copy to René Laporte. In Cologne in 1921 Eluard and Ernst had already collaborated on a book of poems and collages entitled *Répétitions*, which was published in Paris in 1922 (Au Sans Pareil). Together these publications marked Ernst's entry into the Parisian Dada/Surrealist group. His use of late nineteenth-century engravings as the source material for their illustrations anticipates the series of collage novels which opened with *La Femme 100 têtes* in 1929 (no. 104).

100. Au défaut du silence
Paris, 1924
With reproductions of twenty sheets of pen and ink portrait drawings of Gala Eluard by Max Ernst
28.5 × 22.5
No. 12 out of a total edition of 50
Inscribed 'avec l'amitié de Gala'

Gala Eluard later became the wife of Salvador Dalí. Her status as chief 'muse' of the movement in the early 1920s is reflected in this book, and in Ernst's 'family portrait' of the Surrealists, *The rendezvous of friends*, December 1922, where she is the only woman present.

101. Chanson complète
Paris, Gallimard, 1939
With four lithographs by Max Ernst
25.5 × 20
No. 13 out of a special illustrated edition of 20
Inscribed 'Paul Eluard' *and* 'Max Ernst' *on back page*

PAUL ÉLUARD and MAN RAY

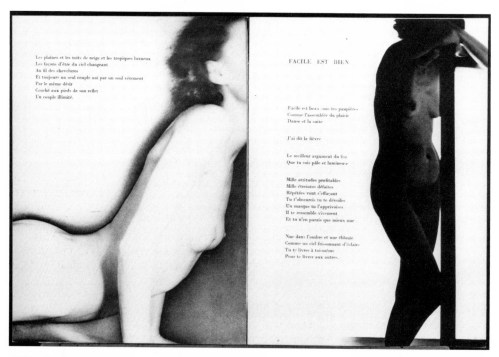

102. Facile
Poèmes de Paul Eluard.
Photographies de Man Ray
Paris, Editions GLM, 1935
24.5 × 18.5

Man Ray has dedicated this copy to Zwemmer (the London book dealer). The model for the photographs was Nusch, Eluard's second wife, and the poems were inspired by his love for her.

MAX ERNST

103. Histoire naturelle
Paris, Editions Jeanne Bucher,
1926
Preface by Hans Arp
50 × 32.5
No. 149 out of a total edition
of 306

The portfolio contains thirty-four collotype plates after pencil *frottages* Ernst made in 1925. Although in 'Au-delà de la peinture' (1936) Ernst dated his fascination with the *frottage* technique from the summer of 1925, he had in fact experimented with it even before moving to Paris, in *Animal head on a plinth*, c. 1921: there the surface rubbed is a plank of wood – so often the starting-point for the *frottages* in the *Histoire naturelle*. In

'Au-delà de la peinture' Ernst comments: 'I emphasise the fact that in the course of a series of spontaneously exposed suggestions and transmutations (like hypnagogical visions), drawings obtained by *frottage* lose more and more the character of the material explored (wood, for example) to take on the aspect of unexpectedly precise images whose nature probably reveals the initial cause of the obsession or a semblance of that cause.'

104. La Femme 100 têtes
Paris, Editions du Carrefour, 1929
Introduction by André Breton
25 × 19
No. 947 out of a total edition of 1000

This copy formerly belonged to Marcel Mariën. The book consists of reproductions of 147 collages with captions by Ernst, plus a reproduction of a collage on the front cover. In earlier collages, Ernst had usually arranged pieces cut out from printed illustrations on a neutral ground, thus arriving at the final image through an additive process. In *La Femme 100 têtes* his method is different: now he takes over a single source image whole, intervening only to add a number of cut pieces to it. He followed this method in the later collage novels.

105. Rêve d'une petite fille qui voulut entrer au Carmel
Paris, Editions du Carrefour, 1930
24 × 19
No. 203 out of a total edition of 1000

This copy formerly belonged to Marcel Mariën. The book consists of an introduction – the only introduction Ernst wrote for any of his collage novels – and reproductions of 79 collages with captions, plus a reproduction of a collage on the cover. Like *La Femme 100 têtes*, it shows a general preoccupation with themes of violence, sexual desire, the Church, journeys etc., and represents a sustained attempt to reproduce the quality and effect of the dream process. The final collage bears the caption: '"Monster! Do you realise I'm in love?!" – End of dream.'

106. Une Semaine de
bonté: ou, Les Sept
éléments capitaux
Paris, Editions Jeanne Bucher,
1934
28 × 22.5
No. 612 out of a total edition
of 812

The 'novel' is divided into five separate, paperbound volumes, each with a soft ground etching as its frontispiece. These were issued individually from April to December 1934, in imitation of the serialisation of popular novels in the nineteenth century. In total there are reproductions of 182 collages, which were created in an astonishing burst of energy during a three-week holiday in Italy in 1933. Unlike the earlier collage novels, *Une Semaine de bonté* has no written captions. Instead Ernst relies on the use of consistent settings and characters to establish some sort of continuity in the 'narrative'. The raw material of the collages remained, however, as banal as ever – pages of engravings from melodramatic pulp fiction of the late nineteenth century, scientific journals and natural history magazines, all of which are transformed into astonishing and disorienting images through the addition of a few alien details.

LISE HIRTZ

107. Il était une
petite pie
7 chansons et 3 chansons pour
Hyacinthe, avec 8 dessins en
couleur par Joan Miró
Paris, Editions Jeanne Bucher, 1928
With illustrations by Joan Miró
32.5 × 25
No. 19 out of a total edition of 300
Inscribed 'Lise Hirtz' and 'Joan Miró' on back page

The portfolio has a cover designed by Miró. His gouaches were reproduced in *pochoir*, each one twice – in black only and in colour. The portfolio bears a general dedication to Georges Auric.

GEORGES HUGNET

108. Onan
Paris, Editions Surréalistes,
1934
With aquatint frontispiece by Salvador Dalí, inscribed 'Salvador Dalí ⁹/₇₇'
34 × 29.5
No. 9 out of a total edition of 277

The Dalí frontispiece did not appear in the regular edition of 200.

109. La Hampe
de l'imaginaire
Paris, GLM, 1936
With etchings by
Oscar Dominguez
26 × 20
Hors commerce copy out
of a total edition of 70
Inscribed 'Guy Lévis-Mano'
on back page

Formerly in the collection of Georges Hugnet. This copy contains the manuscript of his poem 'La Hampe de l'imaginaire' enclosed in its own cover, which has been designed by Hugnet and bears an original collage. The manuscript is dedicated to his wife: 'à Germaine/mon amour/GEORGES/1936'. It is dated 1933. The published text – also dedicated to Germaine Hugnet on the title-page – contains five states of Dominguez's etching (inscribed '²/₅ Nov 1935'). Included loose is an original pencil drawing by Dominguez.

110. La Septième face
du dé
Poèmes. Découpages
Paris, Editions Jeanne
Bucher, 1936
Cover by Marcel Duchamp
29 × 21.5
Unnumbered copy out of
a total edition of 294

Hugnet unites the principal spheres of his artistic activity – poetry and collage – in the twenty 'poem cut-outs' which make up the book. The perfect union of the visual and the verbal, expressed in the concept of *peinture-poésie*, had been an ideal of the Surrealist movement since its earliest beginnings, and remained the motivating force for Hugnet throughout his life. The cover is the one designed by Duchamp for the regular edition, and reproduces his celebrated 'assisted readymade', *Why not sneeze Rose Sélavy?*, 1921.

111. La Septième face
du dé
Dummy of the above item,
1936

Originally in Hugnet's collection. The dummy has as an additional cover the one designed by Duchamp for the twenty de luxe copies of the published book: it is composed from two colour photographs of cigarettes stripped bare.

112. La Chevelure
Paris, Editions Sagesse, 1937
With frontispiece by
Yves Tanguy
21 × 16.5
No. B out of a total edition of 100
Inscribed 'GEORGES HUGNET' and 'Yves Tanguy' on back page

This copy, printed on special burgundy-coloured paper, has a collage cover by Hugnet. The text, which bears a general dedication to Nusch and Paul Eluard, is dated 1934.

113. Une Ecriture lisible
Paris, Editions des Chroniques
du Jour, 1938
With illustrations by
Kurt Seligmann
28 × 23
Unnumbered copy out of a total edition of 255

This copy is dedicated to Jeanne Bucher, the publisher of many important Surrealist books, including several by Hugnet. It is signed by both Hugnet and Seligmann.

114. Non Vouloir
Paris, Editions Jeanne Bucher,
1942
With woodcuts and an aquatint
by Pablo Picasso
19.5 × 14
No. 25 out of a total edition of 426

The woodcuts by Picasso are in four different colour-ways. Hugnet had published an *hors commerce* edition of *Non Vouloir* in 1940.

115. La Femme facile
Paris, Editions Jeanne
Bucher, 1942
With lithograph illustrations by
Christine Boumeester and
Henri Goetz
16.5 × 23.5
Unnumbered copy out of a total edition of 115

This was Hugnet's copy; the cover was designed by him. The text is an extract from *Les Revenants futurs* and has been reproduced lithographically from his handwritten text. *Les Revenants futurs* was published in full, *hors commerce*, in 1952.

116. Le Feu au cul
Paris, published anonymously,
privately printed, 1943
With etchings by Oscar
Dominguez in various
colours, and illustrations
by Dominguez printed over
the text
10.5 × 15.5
No. 1 out of a total edition of 53

This copy was printed specially for Hugnet. It has been bound and cased by him in cream-coloured leather lined with suede, and has decalcomania endpapers by him. The cover of the book has an impressed reproduction of one of Dominguez's illustrations. Dominguez was a close friend of Hugnet, who wrote several exhibition prefaces for him. It was from Dominguez that Hugnet learnt the decalcomania technique. Hugnet's text is dated 1932.

GEORGES HUGNET and HANS BELLMER

117. Œillades ciselées en branche
Paris, Editions Jeanne Bucher, 1939
With illustrations by Hans Bellmer
13.5 × 9.5
Inscribed 'EXEMPLAIRE d'auteur/sur papier azuré ancien/GEORGES/HUGNET/ 1939', *and* 'Hans Bellmer' *on back page*
Total edition of 231

This was Hugnet's copy, and he made for it a deep pink, leather-covered protective box with a collage lining. Each copy of the book, which was designed to be as precious as a Valentine or an illuminated manuscript, had a pink cover to which was fixed a white paper doily, and each had a different *fin-de-siècle* coloured paper scrap attached to the top right-hand corner. The first thirty copies (including this one) were printed on special paper, impregnated with perfume. The book contains a prose poem by Hugnet, printed from the author's handwritten text, and inspired by Bellmer's Doll. It is illustrated with twenty-five drawings by Bellmer in shades of pink, olive green, russet, mauve etc. (The original pencil sketch for one of the drawings is no. 4.) The title (Bunches cut on the branch) was 'found' in true Surrealist manner by a friend who saw it written on the label of some grapes hanging in a greengrocer's shop: it particularly delighted Bellmer and Hugnet because of the double meaning of 'œillades' in French – bunches/lascivious glances.

GEORGES HUGNET and VIRGIL THOMSON

118. La Belle en dormant
Poèmes de Georges Hugnet pour voix de mezzo-soprano ou baryton
Manuscript by Thomson, 1931. Binding by Hugnet
With etchings by Louis Marcoussis
35 × 27
Inscribed 'histoire d'amitié/ pour Georges Hugnet/son fidèle/Virgil' *on title-page*

The four poems included in this manuscript are 'Pour chercher sur la carte des mers', 'La première de toutes', 'Mon amour est bon à dire', and 'Partis les vaisseaux'. Each of them has been set to music by the American composer and pianist Virgil Thomson, and each is inscribed by him 'VGGT Villefranche-s-mer', and dated variously from 20 August to 1 October 1931. The manuscript is bound in pink cloth, and has decalcomania endpapers by Hugnet, each inscribed 'GH 1933'. This date may, however, relate to the date of publication of Hugnet's poems (*La Belle en dormant*, Paris, Editions des Cahiers Libres, 1933) rather than to the date of the binding, which was probably several years later. The book also incorporates an etching by Marcoussis in three different states. The first state is inscribed '1/4' and 'à Georges Hugnet en très amical souvenir L.M.'. The two other states are unsigned. Hugnet had first met Thomson in Paris in the winter of 1926–27, and they became close friends – a friendship commemorated in this collaboration.

ANDRÉ JEAN and MARCEL JEAN

119. Mourir pour la patrie
Paris, Editions des Cahiers d'Art, 1935; 33 × 25.5
No. 103 out of a total edition of 210

A collection of twenty-four drawings and a preface by Marcel Jean, with captions by André Jean.

MARCEL JEAN

120. Pêche pour le sommeil jeté
Manuscript, 1935
With two etchings by Marcel Jean
32.5 × 25

This was formerly in the collection of Georges Hugnet. It is the manuscript of Jean's poems, together with various states of his etchings. It is dedicated to Hugnet by the author and the dedication is dated '8/1/35'. The etchings also bear dedications to Hugnet. The binding, with decalcomania endpapers, is by Hugnet and has a leather insert on the cover with the title, an illustration by Jean, and the date '1935'. *Pêche pour le sommeil jeté* was published in 1937 (Paris, Editions Sagesse). Marcel Jean became an important figure in the Surrealist movement in the 1930s. He was the maker of a number of celebrated objects, including *The spectre of the gardenia*, 1936, a dummy-head, with zipper eyes and a roll of film round its neck, and has been the author of important histories of the movement, including the now classic *History of Surrealist Painting*, 1960.

COMTE DE LAUTRÉAMONT (Isidore Ducasse)

121. Les Chants de Maldoror
Paris, Albert Skira, 1934
With fifty-two original etchings by Salvador Dalí
33 × 25.5
No. 28 out of a total projected edition of 270
Inscribed 'Salvador Dalí'

The response to the initial 'advertisement to subscribers' was disappointing, and in the event only about half the number of projected copies of the book was published. Skira was a brilliant young Swiss publisher who, with Tériade, was responsible for launching what became the most important Surrealist review of the later 1930s, *Minotaure* (1933–39: see no. 164). *Les Chants de Maldoror* was the single most important pre-Surrealist text in the eyes of the Surrealists themselves. Ducasse, the self-styled Comte de Lautréamont, had published the full text of his extraordinary epic prose poem in Brussels in 1869 and in Paris in 1874, but copies of it and of his *Poésies* remained extremely scarce until the future Surrealists began their concerted campaign to establish his reputation. In 1919 Breton published the *Poésies* in *Littérature* (nos. 2 and 3), and from then on Lautréamont and his works were repeatedly quoted, praised and analysed. As Breton explained in an interview given in 1952: 'For us there was no other genius who could stand comparison with Lautréamont' (*Entretiens 1913–1952 avec André Parinaud*, Paris, 1952, p. 43). In 1925 Philippe Soupault edited his complete writings, and in 1938 the Surrealists published a de luxe edition of the complete works with illustrations by the leading painters in the group, including Dalí.

122. Quelques écrits
et quelques dessins de
Clarisse Juranville
Brussels, René Henriquez,
1927
With illustrations by Magritte
16 × 12
No. 99 out of a total edition of 110

Published under the name of Clarisse Juranville, the poems by Nougé, the leader of the Belgian Surrealist group, were 'inspired' by the popular Larousse manuals of French grammar by Mlle. Juranville. Magritte illustrated the poems with five drawings. They were subsequently put to music by André Souris, another leading member of the Brussels group.

(no. 123)

123. [Le Catalogue
Samuel]
Brussels, Bischoffsheim, 1927
With illustrations by Magritte
22 × 15.5

This is the catalogue issued by the *Maison Samuel* 'pour l'année 1928' (for the 1928 season). The previous year Magritte had made the illustrations for a catalogue for the same firm of Brussels furriers. On that occasion the accompanying commentary had, apparently, been written by Camille Goemans. This time Magritte asked Paul Nougé to write the texts to accompany his publicity designs. The result of their collaboration is this remarkable brochure, illustrated with reproductions (two in colour) of sixteen collages by Magritte, which are closely related to his contemporary paintings. His admiration for the work of de Chirico and of the Ernst of the early 1920s is evident, but many specifically Magrittian motifs are present, such as the curtain and the turned wooden skittle or baluster.

ALICE PAALEN

124. Sablier couché
Paris, Editions Sagesse, 1938
With frontispiece by
Joan Miró
21.5 × 17
No. 72 out of a total edition
of 75
Inscribed 'Alice Paalen'
on back page

This copy is dedicated to Hugnet by both Alice Paalen and Miró, who has added a drawing in pencil and coloured crayons dated '1.39' on the front page. It also contains the deleted proof of Miró's frontispiece, inscribed 'Miró/épreuve rayée/⅕.'. The author was married to Wolfgang Paalen, a painter from Vienna who joined the Surrealist group in Paris in about 1935.

EDUARDO PAOLOZZI

125. Metafisikal
Translations
Screenprinted by Kelpra
Studio Limited,
December 1962
30 × 21.5
No. 2 out of a total edition
of 100

This copy has a dedication by the author. Partly a key to his contemporary work in other media and to his preoccupations as an artist, the book is also an extension of his use of collage onto a verbal/literary plane. Sections of the text, for example, collapse conventional syntax and play with spelling so that the meaning of the juxtaposed phrases becomes highly ambiguous and the effect is of collage-poetry. The text itself is set in different typefaces and in some sections reproduces Paolozzi's own written or printed notes. There is a family link between *Metafisikal Translations* and Duchamp's *Green box* (no. 96) and the poems and manifestos of the Dadaists.

HENRI PASTOUREAU

126. Le Corps trop
grand pour un cerceuil
Paris, Editions Surréalistes,
1936
Preface by André Breton
With frontispiece by Giorgio de Chirico
25.5 × 15.5
No. 1 out of a total edition of 200

This copy contains the manuscripts of Pastoureau's poems and Breton's preface. It also contained the original drawing by de Chirico reproduced as the frontispiece. That drawing is no. 8.

127. L'Amour n'est pas pour nous, suivi de Femme magique
Paris, Editions de la Main à Plume, 1942
With a 'Portrait automatique de l'auteur' by Noël Arnaud, and two drawings by Tita
19.3 × 14.5
No. 1 out of a total·edition of 220

This copy is dedicated: 'à l'ami de Paul Eluard/l'ami de Georges Hugnet/Marc Patin'. It includes the manuscripts of Patin's texts and Arnaud's 'automatic portrait', and additional original coloured drawings by Tita. Noël Arnaud was one of the new younger Surrealists who made strenuous efforts to keep the movement in Paris going during the occupation, when so many of the older, founder members were in voluntary 'exile' in America or elsewhere. Under the title of Editions de la Main à Plume he published a number of 'collective plaquettes' – essentially ephemeral reviews – among the most important of which was *La Conquête du Monde par l'Image*. This came out in April 1942, with a photograph of Picasso's *Bull's head* (created from the seat and handlebars of a bicycle) on the cover; among the contributors were Patin, Tita, Arnaud, Eluard and Hugnet.

ROLAND PENROSE

128. The Road is wider than long
London, London Gallery Editions, 1939
21 × 17
No. ∞ out of a total edition of 510

Penrose's text is subtitled 'An Image Diary from the Balkans, July–August 1938', and illustrated with his photographs. Extracts had been published in *London Bulletin* no. 7, December 1938–January 1939. The cover of the book was designed by Bellmer. This copy has a dedication by the author.

BENJAMIN PÉRET

129. Au 125 du Boule-vard Saint-Germain
Paris, Collection Littérature,
1923
With drypoint frontispiece by
Max Ernst, and reproductions
of three drawings by Péret
16 × 11
Total edition of 181

Péret has dedicated this copy to René Coroller on the title-page. Péret was one of the founder members of the Surrealist group and, with Pierre Naville, edited *La Révolution Surréaliste* from its foundation until July 1925, when Breton took control. He was particularly close to Breton, and remained an active collaborator in Surrealist activities until his death in 1959.

130. Je ne mange pas de ce pain-là
Paris, Editions Surréalistes, 1936
With drypoint frontispiece by Max Ernst
22.5 × 16.5
No. 37 out of a total edition of 250

131. Je sublime
Paris, Editions Surréalistes, 1936
With frottage *illustrations by Max Ernst*
19 × 22
No. 6 out of a total edition of 241

132. La Brebis galante
Paris, Editions Premières,
1949
With illustrations by
Max Ernst
24 × 19.5
No. 281 out of a total edition of 316

Ernst's illustrations consist of: three etchings with aquatint which are printed in colour; reproductions of twenty-two drawings with collage, of which eighteen are coloured with *pochoir*; and an original lithographic cover. This copy was formerly in the collection of Joe Tilson.

BENJAMIN PÉRET and LOUIS ARAGON

133. 1929
No publisher cited, 1929
With four photographs
by Man Ray
31 × 23.5
No. 44 out of a total edition of 215

Péret was responsible for the 'Premier semestre' (January–June), and Aragon for the 'Deuxième semestre' (July–September). The notorious Kiki de Montparnasse, a model often used by Man Ray, posed with Man Ray for the photographs.

FRANCIS PICABIA

134. Poèmes et dessins de la fille née sans mère
Lausanne, Imprimeries
Réunies S.A., 1918
24 × 16

There are fifty-one poems and eighteen drawings in this collection. They were mostly composed in Switzerland in the spring of 1918 while Picabia was under treatment for a neurasthenic condition.

135. Râteliers platoniques
Poème en deux chapîtres
Lausanne, 1918
22 × 22.5

The book bears a general dedication to Apollinaire, who died in November 1918. This copy is dedicated twice by Picabia, first to Paul Eluard (on 1 December 1922), secondly to Georges Hugnet (on 31 October 1947). It includes original watercolour and gouache drawings by Picabia: one shows a naked woman pleading with a man in striped pyjamas (inscribed 'Francis Picabia'); the other, on the verso, is an abstract 'automatic' gouache (inscribed 'Francis Picabia Juillet 1923').

136. Jésus-Christ Rastaquouère
Paris, Au Sans Pareil, 1920
With illustrations by Georges Ribemont-Dessaignes
Introduction by Gabrielle Buffet
24.5 × 18.5
No. 17 out of a total edition of 1060
Signed by Gabrielle Buffet-Picabia

The blasphemous title (roughly translatable as 'Jesus Christ, flashy foreign adventurer') and certain passages in the book got Picabia into trouble with his publishers. Breton intervened on his behalf, and it was published without censorship. But he refused to write the preface he had promised. Furious, Picabia quarrelled with him and got his wife to write one in his place. Ribemont-Dessaignes was a close ally of Picabia's in the Parisian Dada group, sharing his iconoclastic and nihilistic attitudes, and, like him, enjoying a stormy relationship with Breton.

137. La Loi d'accommodation chez les borgnes 'Sursum Corda'
Film en trois parties
Paris, Editions Th. Briant, 1928
28 × 22.5
No. 35 out of a total edition of 365

A film scenario with lithographic illustrations by Picabia. In his preface Picabia exhorts the reader/spectator to 'roll' the film himself – he can watch it even from his bed, 'the seats are all the same price, and you can smoke without annoying your neighbour'. Each, he continues, must see the film on 'the screen of his imagination', which is 'infinitely superior' to the 'wretched' screen of the ordinary cinema. Picabia's interest in film was lifelong. In 1924 he had contributed the scenario for René Clair's *Entr'acte*, and had also appeared in it alongside, among others, Erik Satie.

138. Exposition Francis Picabia
Introductory texts by Emile Fabre and Emeran Clémansin du Maine
Cannes, Cercle Nautique, 28 January–7 February 1927
25.5 × 19.5
No. 51 out of a total edition of 200
Inscribed 'Francis Picabia'

This copy includes an original wash drawing by Picabia of a nude female fencer.

MAN RAY

139. Revolving doors
Paris, Editions Surréalistes, 1926; 53 × 35
No. 6 out of a total edition of 105
Inscribed 'Man Ray'

The ten *pochoirs* in the portfolio reproduce ten coloured paper collages Man Ray had executed in New York in 1916–17. They are titled as follows: I Mime; II Long distance; III Orchestra; IV The meeting; V Legend; VI Decanter; VII Jeune fille; VIII Shadows; IX Concrete mixer; X Dragonfly. They were derived ultimately from the large flat coloured shapes in his major painting of 1916, *The rope dancer accompanies herself with her shadows*. In 1919, at Daniel's Gallery in New York, Man Ray had exhibited the original collages of *Revolving doors* on a hinged, revolving stand, and written a fanciful, proto-Surrealist text to accompany them. He exhibited them again at his one-man show at the Galerie Surréaliste in Paris in 1926. The *pochoir* reproductions were published to coincide with that show. In 1916 he had made painted versions of a couple of the collages; in 1942 he made painted replicas of all ten of them.

140. La Photographie n'est pas l'art
Paris, GLM, 1937
Text by André Breton
25 × 16.5

With twelve recent photographs by Man Ray. Breton's text, 'Convulsionnaire', takes the form of surrealistic aphorisms.

MAN RAY and PAUL ÉLUARD

141. Les Mains libres
Dessins de Man Ray illustrés par les poèmes de Paul Eluard
Paris, Editions Jeanne Bucher, 1937
28.5 × 23
No. 265 out of a total edition of 675

Man Ray had left the drawings reproduced in this book with Eluard, who, within a period of a few weeks, produced the suite of poems inspired by them. The title contains a pun on the artist's name – 'main'/Man – and alludes to his avowed principles of liberty and pleasure. This copy is dedicated to Jacques-Henri Levêsque by Man Ray. Inserted beside each drawing is a sheet with a manuscript poem of 2–8 lines in an unidentified hand.

GEORGE REAVEY

142. Faust's Metamorphoses
Fontenay-aux-Roses, The New Review Editions, 1932
With six engravings by Stanley William Hayter
Foreword by Samuel Putnam
26 × 20
No. 40 out of a total edition of 136
Inscribed 'George Reavey' and 'SW Hayter' on back page

Hayter, an English painter and engraver, moved to Paris in 1926 and the following year founded his *Atelier 17*, which quickly became established as one of the most innovative and significant printmaking studios. He had numerous 'pupils', including Ernst, Chagall and Giacometti. He was closely associated with the Surrealists in the 1930s, sharing their fascination with chance effects and radical procedures, which he exploited in his own prints. George Reavey was involved in the Surrealist movement in England in the 1930s, and contributed to *London Bulletin*.

ANDRÉ THIRION

143. Le Grand ordinaire
Paris, [1943]
With two original etchings and eight original pen and ink drawings
20 × 15
Unnumbered hors commerce *copy out of a total edition of 128*

Le Grand ordinaire was published anonymously and clandestinely during the occupation in 1943, but bears the date 1934. This copy is one of seven *hors commerce* copies printed on two-colour scarlet and emerald paper, and is dedicated at length on the title-page to Georges Hugnet by André Thirion (dedication dated 25 February 1944). It includes eight full-page original pen and ink drawings in addition to the printed illustrations, and the two original (loose) etchings. The artist(s) has not been identified. It also includes an envelope containing some of Thirion's official wartime documents, variously dated 1943–45, together with a manuscript page in his hand listing the projected contents of *Paris se repeuple*. Thirion had been an active member of the Surrealist group, but became estranged from Breton in the 1930s as his commitment to specifically political action grew. He has described the dilemmas within the Surrealist movement over the issue of adherence to the Communist Party in *Révolutionnaires sans Révolution*, Paris, 1972. Hugnet had long been a close friend, but was outraged by what he regarded as the serious misrepresentations in Thirion's book: a long review denouncing the 'imposture' is published in his *Pleins et déliés*, Paris, 1972 (pp. 392–415).

TRISTAN TZARA

144. vingt-cinq poèmes
Zurich, Collection Dada, 1918
With ten woodcuts by Hans Arp
20.5 × 14.5

This copy has a dedication by Tzara. The poems gathered here date from 1915–18. Tzara, a Rumanian poet and critic, was one of the most important animators of the whole Dada movement, and, with Hugo Ball, its leader in Zurich during the First World War. In Paris from 1920 onwards he contested the leadership of Parisian Dada with Breton, opposing those tendencies which led eventually to the emergence of Surrealism. Later he and Breton were reconciled, and Tzara – like Arp – became an important figure in the Surrealist movement. The illustrations created by Arp to accompany Tzara's Dada poems are justly celebrated: they reflect the influence upon him of Kandinsky's woodcuts in *Klänge* (Munich, 1913), but are also highly characteristic of the personal 'biomorphic' style of the great series of wooden reliefs initiated during the war.

145. L'Antitête
Paris, Editions des Cahiers Libres, 1933
With frontispiece etching by Pablo Picasso
20 × 15.5
No. 14 out of a total edition of 1218
Signed by Tzara and Picasso

Tzara has dedicated this copy to Georges Hugnet, and has added a pen and ink surrealistic drawing.

VARIOUS AUTHORS

146. Violette Nozières
Brussels, Editions Nicolas Flamel, 1933
With contributions by:
André Breton, René Char,
Paul Eluard, Maurice Henry,
E. L. T. Mesens, César Moró,
Benjamin Péret, Gui Rosey,
Salvador Dalí, Yves Tanguy,
Max Ernst, Victor Brauner,
René Magritte, Marcel Jean,
Hans Arp and Alberto Giacometti
19.5 × 14.5

A miscellany of writings and drawings by members of the Paris and Brussels Surrealist groups in honour of Violette Nozières, the murderess whose trial had excited widespread public interest. A fascination with violent crime, as with insanity, was an article of faith with the Surrealists. Those who committed crimes of passion, especially if they were women, aroused their enthusiastic admiration. In the very first issue of *La Révolution Surréaliste*, December 1924, photo-portraits of the members of the group surround a much larger photograph of Germaine Berton, an anarchist who had murdered the leader of an extreme right-wing group. Like Germaine Berton, Violette Nozières has become their Muse.

L'Impromptu de Versailles

(no. 146)

Periodicals and Exhibition Catalogues

N.B. *The reader is referred to Dawn Ades,* Dada and Surrealism Reviewed, *Arts Council of Great Britain, 1978, for a detailed account of many of the periodicals listed below.*

147. Arson. An ardent review. Part One of a Surrealist manifestation
London, March 1942
ed. Toni del Renzio
28 × 22

No other part was published because there was no money forthcoming. *Arson* was the first Surrealist review to come out in England after *London Bulletin* ceased publication in June 1940. It was dedicated to Surrealists all over the world at a time of crisis and dispersal, and mainly comprised new contributions by members of the English group and extracts or reprints from texts by leading French Surrealists, including Breton.

148. Axis: A quarterly review of contemporary 'abstract' painting and sculpture
London, 1935–37
ed. Myfanwy Evans
Eight numbers
27.5 × 21.5

Myfanwy Evans had visited Jean Hélion's studio in Paris and been urged by him to found a review in England which would accommodate abstract and constructivist art. *Axis* was the result. It is ideologically close to *Abstraction-Création* in France and many of the same artists were represented in it, including Hélion and Arp, as well as Hepworth and Nicholson.

149. Bifur
Paris, 1929–31
ed. Georges Ribemont-Dessaignes
Eight numbers
23.5 × 19

Ribemont-Dessaignes had been a leader of Parisian Dada, and *Bifur* published texts by many of his old Dada comrades, including Tzara, Soupault and Picabia. It also became a forum for the dissident Surrealists, including Jacques Baron, Desnos, Michel Leiris and Georges Limbour.

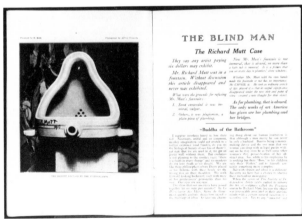

150. P.B.T.
The Blind Man
No. 2, New York, May 1917
ed. Marcel Duchamp
28 × 20

The second of only two issues of *The Blind Man*, its main focus is the scandal surrounding Duchamp's *Fountain* – an upended urinal signed 'R. MUTT 1917' – which had been rejected by the hanging committee of the supposedly liberal and avant-garde New Society for Independent Artists.

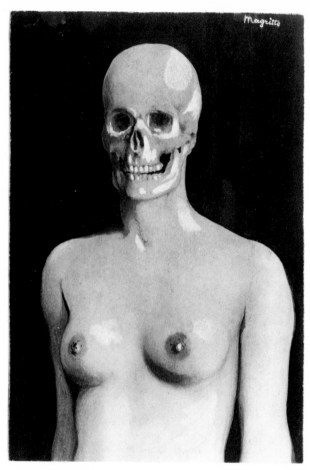

151. Bulletin
International du
Surréalisme
No. 3, Brussels,
20 August, 1935
No. 4, London,
September 1936
29 × 20.5

The Belgian edition of the *Bulletin* has Magritte's *La gâcheuse* (no. 40) on the cover and features a manifesto signed by all the leading Belgian Surrealists. The English edition celebrated the International Surrealist Exhibition held in London during June–July 1936 and the official foundation of an English branch of the Surrealist movement. The first two *Bulletins* had been published in Prague in April 1935 and Santa Cruz de Tenerife in October 1935. The latter commemorated the Surrealist exhibition held there that May.

152. Cannibale
Paris, 1920
ed. Francis Picabia
Two numbers
24 × 16

Picabia temporarily interrupted publication of *391* to bring out the two issues of *Cannibale* in April and May 1920. His aim was to produce a definitive international Dada review 'with the collaboration of all the Dadaists in the world', but by July, when he brought out the thirteenth issue of *391*, he had come to see this as an 'impossible' and 'stupid' ambition.

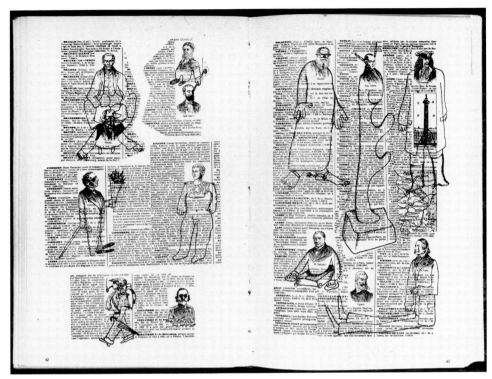

153. Documents 34
Brussels, 1934
ed. Stéphanie Cordier and
E. L. T. Mesens
24 × 16.5

Documents 34, issued in June 1934, is subtitled 'Intervention Surréaliste'. It contains contributions by members of both the Belgian and Parisian Surrealist groups, who were at this period in complete accord about the need actively to combat Fascism and the right of the movement to act independently of the official Communist Party.

154. First papers of
Surrealism
New York, Coordinating
Council of French Relief
Societies, Inc.,
October–November 1942
26.5 × 18.5

The catalogue of the Surrealist exhibition organised by Breton and other members of the Surrealist group in New York in aid of French children and prisoners. The title alludes to an immigrant's first naturalisation papers, and the front cover designed by Duchamp is a photograph of a pitted wall pierced by five bullet holes (the paper is perforated to conform to the shots). Duchamp was also entrusted with the installation of the show, and created an immense and tangled web out of miles of white string stretching from room to room, and masking not only the nineteenth-century interior but also the Surrealist works on display.

155. 491
Paris, 4 March 1949
ed. Michel Tapié
65 × 50

491, which is designed to resemble closely the format and typography of Picabia's *391* (see no. 172), is in fact the catalogue of the Picabia retrospective organised by Michel Tapié at the Galerie René Drouin in Paris under the title '50 ans de plaisir'.

There were contributions by, among others, Breton, Gabrielle Buffet, Jean Cocteau, Olga Picabia and Desnos.

156. Le Grand Jeu
Paris, 1928–30
ed. R.Gilbert-Lecomte, R.Dau-
mal, J. Simon, R. Vaillard
Three numbers
24 × 19

The review of a para-Surrealist group who had taken the title from a book of poems by Péret published in 1928. The *Grand Jeu* group were criticised by the Surrealists around Breton for their inclination to purely literary and artistic activity, and were suspected of political compromise.

157. L'Invention Collective
Brussels, 1940
ed. Raoul Ubac
Two numbers
23.5 × 17.5

The only two issues of *L'Invention Collective* came out in February and April 1940: the fall of Belgium and France made continuation impossible. The review was founded 'on the dark threshold of 1940' in order 'to guard intact the state of mind which Surrealism has created'. The initiative came from Magritte and Raoul Ubac, and under their influence there was an emphasis on Surrealist painting and photography. Alongside theirs the work of Delvaux and members of the Belgian Surrealist group was featured. Magritte's 'La Ligne de vie', an account of the development of his work, was published in the second issue, which also contained contributions by Breton.

158. Konkretion. Inter-skandinavisktidsskrift for kunsten af i dag
Copenhagen, Oslo,
Stockholm, 1935–36
ed. V. Bjerke-Petersen
Nos. 3 and 5–6
23 × 14.5

Issue no. 3, November 1935, was devoted to 'English art today' and included translations of texts by Herbert Read, David Gascoyne and Geoffrey Grigson. The cover featured a sculpture by Henry Moore. Nos. 5–6, March 1936, subtitled 'Surrealism in Paris', reprinted in translation many texts by leading poets and painters in the Surrealist group. The review reflects the general currency of avant-garde movements throughout the Western world in the 1930s.

159. Littérature
Paris, 1919–24
ed. A. Breton, L. Aragon
P. Soupault
First series: twenty numbers,
March 1919–August 1921,
23 × 14
New series: thirteen numbers,
March 1922–June 1924,
23.5 × 18
ILLUSTRATION ON P. 6

Littérature, which began life as an avant-garde review with an allegiance to Symbolist and post-Symbolist traditions in recent French literature, was gradually taken over by Dada – a process which was complete by May 1920, when the entire thirteenth issue was devoted to the publication of twenty-three Dada manifestos. In the event, the commitment to Dada was relatively short-lived, as the antagonism between Breton and Tzara – the very voice of Dada – developed. The publication of the new series of the review marks the change as the ideas and methods which became the bedrock of early Surrealism crystallised. In 'Entrée des Médiums', an important essay published in November 1922, Breton is already defining Surrealism in terms of a 'certain psychic automatism which corresponds quite well to the dream state' – a definition which is essentially the same as that given in the first Surrealist manifesto in October 1924. Apart from Breton himself and his poet friends, a dominant presence in the new series was Picabia, who designed a number of brilliant and arresting covers.

160. The Little Review
New York, Autumn–Winter
1923–24
ed. Margaret Anderson and
Jane Heap
24 × 19

Perhaps the most widely known and respected avant-garde literary and artistic periodical to be produced in America at the period, *The Little Review* ran from 1914 to 1929. During the years 1920–24 many of the leading members of Parisian Dada contributed to it, among them Aragon, Breton, Eluard, Picabia and Tzara: the issue on display is largely occupied by their texts. It was also a major forum for the modern movement in America. (Ezra Pound was for a period assistant editor.)

161. London Bulletin
London, 1938–40
ed. E. L. T. Mesens, with,
variously, Humphrey
Jennings, Roland Penrose,
George Reavey, Gordon
Onslow-Ford
Twenty numbers
25 × 19

Published by the London Gallery, this was the official review of the English Surrealist group, although the commitment to Surrealism was never exclusive. Thus the double issue devoted to 'Living Art in England' (nos. 8–9, January–February 1939) featured, beside the Surrealists, those who described themselves as Independents, Constructivists or Abstract artists.

162. La Main à Plume
Paris, Editions de la Main
à Plume, 1941
ed. Marc Patin
20 × 14

This copy is no. 1 of the special edition of fifty published on coloured paper. It includes an original etching by Vuillamy printed in four different colour-ways, dated 1941. The texts and illustrations are annotated in pencil to identify the authors. The Editions de la Main à Plume was run by Noël Arnaud and, under different titles, published a number of 'plaquettes collectives' between 1941 and 1943. Marc Patin was a regular contributor to these.

163. Marie. Journal
bimensuel pour la belle
jeunesse
Brussels, 1926
ed. E. L. T. Mesens
Three numbers
32.5 × 25

In tenor a Dada periodical, featuring the work of Picabia, Tzara, Ribemont-Dessaignes and Man Ray, as well as that of future members of the Belgian Surrealist group (Magritte, Mesens and Marcel Lecomte in particular).

164. Minotaure
Paris, 1933–39
Director-Administrator
Albert Skira, Artistic Director
E. Tériade
Thirteen numbers
31.5 × 24.5

Far from being envisaged as the new Surrealist review to replace *Le Surréalisme au Service de la Révolution*, *Minotaure* was originally planned as the forum for the dissident Surrealists who had gathered around Georges Bataille. However, it was gradually taken over by Breton and his friends and became to all intents and purposes a Surrealist review, even though non-Surrealists continued to be featured in it. Lavishly produced, beautifully illustrated, each issue with its own specially designed cover by a leading artist, *Minotaure* is a splendid testimony to the richness of the culture of Surrealism in the 1930s.

165. Proverbe. Feuille mensuelle
Paris, 1920–21
ed. Paul Eluard
Six numbers
22.5 × 14

Consisting of a single folded sheet, *Proverbe* was a Dadaist review that published texts by, among others, Aragon, Breton, Eluard, Picabia and Tzara. The first five issues came out monthly from February to May 1920, and the sixth and last in July 1921 under the title *L'Invention no. 1 et Proverbe no. 6.*

166. La Révolution Surréaliste
Paris, 1924–29
Twelve numbers
29 × 20

The first three issues were edited by Pierre Naville and Benjamin Péret (December 1924–April 1925), the remainder by André Breton. The Surrealist movement was launched in October 1924 with the publication of Breton's *Manifeste du Surréalisme.* La Révolution Surréaliste was its official organ, the final issue (December 1929) closing with Breton's Second Manifesto. From the outset much more space was devoted to the visual arts than had been the case in *Littérature:* there were articles such as Breton's seminal essay 'Le Surréalisme et la peinture', and the layout was adroitly devised to play off the visual and the verbal against each other. The changing membership of the group during the five-year lifespan of the review is clearly articulated in the famous montages of photo-portraits reproduced in the first and the last issues.

167. Salvo for Russia
Limited edition of new poems, etchings and engravings produced in aid of the Comforts Fund for Women and Children of Soviet Russia
London, 1942?
23 × 16.5
No. 46 out of a total edition of 100

The writers and artists who collaborated on this plaquette were: Mackworth, Forsyth, J. F. Hendry, Nancy Cunard, John Banting, John Buckland-Wright, Ithell Colquhoun, Roland Penrose, John Piper, Dolf Reiser, Julian Trevelyan, Mary Wykeham. Every illustration was signed by the artist.

168. SIC
Paris, 1916–19
ed. Paul Albert-Birot
Fifty-four numbers
28 × 22.5

An important avant-garde review which published the work of a wide spectrum of writers of the prewar generation (including Reverdy, and Apollinaire, to whom a special issue, nos. 37–39, was devoted), and of younger poets who would be leaders of Parisian Dada after the war.

169. Le Surréalisme en 1929
Special out-of-series number of Variétés
Brussels, June 1929
ed. P. G. Van Hecke
25 × 18
ILLUSTRATION ON P. 80

Most of the leading members of the Paris and Brussels Surrealist groups contributed to this publication, which is richly illustrated and has a visually provocative layout similar to that adopted in *La Révolution Surréaliste.* One of the most memorable items is the 'Surrealist map of the world' which completely redefines geography in terms of the particular preoccupations and predilections of the group: Alaska, Labrador, Mexico, and the South Sea islands dominate, while Europe has shrunk to a pathetic growth from the edge of an enormous Russia. (See also no. 176.)

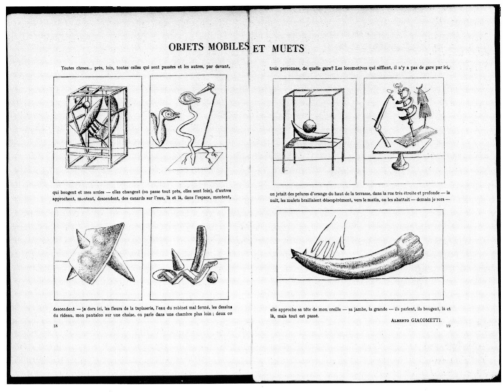

170. Le Surréalisme au Service de la Révolution
Paris, 1930–33
ed. André Breton
Six numbers
28 × 19.5

The sequel to *La Révolution Surréaliste* and, as the change in title implies, a more politically oriented publication altogether, which reflects the often strained relationship between the Surrealists and the French Communist Party. Produced in the straitened financial climate after the Crash, *SASDLR* has far fewer illustrations, and these are for the most part gathered at the back of each issue. Nevertheless, the great importance Breton attached to recent artist-recruits, in particular Dalí and Giacometti, is revealed in the texts and in the illustrations chosen, and emphasis is given to the Surrealist Object as a major new creative avenue.

171. Le Surréalisme, même
Paris, 1956–59
ed. André Breton
Five numbers
19.5 × 19.5

This review, together with *Néon* (1948–49) and *Médium* (1953–55), gives the most complete representation of Surrealist preoccupations in the postwar years. The work of the many new younger members is featured, but the 'old guard' is still in evidence. For instance, Duchamp created a highly provocative cover for the first issue – appropriately so since the title of the review employs the same pun as he had in *La mariée mise à nu par ces célibataires, même*.

172. 391

Barcelona, New York,
Zurich, Paris, 1917–24
ed. Francis Picabia
Nineteen numbers, plus a
supplement entitled Pilhao-
Thibaou
Various dimensions

The most long-lived of the true Dada periodicals, the different places of publication of *391* correspond to the peregrinations of Picabia during this period. The first four issues came out in Barcelona (January–March 1917), nos. 5–7 in New York (June–August 1917), no. 8 in Zurich (February 1919), and the remainder in Paris (November 1919–October 1924). *391* is dominated by Picabia's personality and reproduces many of his contemporary drawings, manifestos and poems. Its layout is always visually exciting and unpredictable, and its tone frequently satirical and nihilistic. Picabia's allegiances are also accurately mirrored – whether his undeviating friendship with Duchamp or his bumpy relationship with Breton.

173. Transfusion du Verbe

Paris, Editions de la Main
à Plume, December 1941
ed. Noël Arnaud
26 × 20
Unnumbered copy out of a total edition of 400

One of several 'plaquettes collectives' issued by Noël Arnaud during the occupation, it features the work of, among others, Arnaud himself, Eluard, Marc Patin, Picasso, Dominguez, Ubac, Tita and Vuillamy. (See also no. 162.)

174. Transition
Paris, 1927–38
ed. Eugene Jolas and
Elliot Paul
Twenty-seven numbers

The major English language periodical edited in France between the wars. It published a number of texts by the Surrealists and the dissidents.

175. 291
New York, 1915–16
ed. Arthur Stieglitz
Twelve numbers
Various dimensions

Named after Stieglitz's 291 Gallery in New York, *291* was planned from the outset to be experimental, to have a strictly limited lifespan, and to be dedicated to the most avant-garde tendencies in contemporary art. The instigator was Marius de Zayas, who had recently returned from Paris and was fully conversant with new artistic trends there. (He was also responsible for several exhibitions of contemporary French art at the 291 Gallery.) *291* exerted a considerable influence on later Dadaist reviews, partly because of its abrasive satirical tone and partly because of its highly experimental typography. Picabia was a regular contributor, and some of his early machine drawings were illustrated in its pages, including his portrait of Stieglitz as a camera (nos. 5–6, July–August 1915, cover). His own review, *391*, was consciously modelled upon it.

176. Variétés
Brussels, 1928–30
ed. P. G. Van Hecke
Twenty-five numbers
25 × 18

Van Hecke was a leading dealer in contemporary Belgian art, and *Variétés*, perhaps the most important vanguard literary and artistic journal of its time in Belgium, was committed – as the cover announced – to the support of 'the contemporary spirit'. It had no allegiance to any particular style or movement, although Van Hecke's special interest in Expressionism is revealed in the generous space allocated to artists like Permeke. In 1927 Van Hecke had written a major article on Magritte (published in *Sélection*, another Brussels review of which he was co-editor), and Magritte was accordingly represented in *Variétés* from time to time by illustrations of recent works. The growing influence of Surrealism in Belgium during the lifespan of the review is reflected in the decision to devote the whole of a special issue to the movement in June 1929 (see no. 169).

177. View
New York, 1940–47
ed. Charles Henri Ford
Thirty-seven numbers
30.5 × 23

View was always a broadly based periodical, committed to no particular contemporary movement. Nevertheless, there was considerable sympathy with Surrealism, and when the Surrealists arrived in New York in 1941–42 they found a natural home in its pages. One of the main contributors, Nicolas Calas, became a close friend of Breton, and special issues were devoted to Ernst (April 1942) and to Tanguy (May 1942), while Masson was regularly represented and was responsible for several covers. One of the most memorable issues of the magazine is the one devoted to Duchamp (March 1945), who designed its cover himself.

178. VVV

New York, 1942–44
ed. David Hare, with
André Breton, Max Ernst
and Marcel Duchamp as
editorial advisers
Four numbers
28 × 21.5

VVV, founded in June 1942, was the rallying-point of the Surrealists in New York and accurately reflects the preoccupations of the movement as a whole during the 1940s. In the first issue Breton published his 'Prolegomena to a third manifesto of Surrealism or else'. Although much less luxurious, *VVV* was modelled on *Minotaure* and carried articles on a great variety of subjects alongside the work of Surrealist poets and painters. Each issue had a specially designed cover, Ernst providing the first and Roberto Matta (a relatively recent recruit) the last. The cover of the 2/3 double issue (March 1943) was created by Duchamp – an elaborate construction in which the back cover has an insert of chicken wire over a hole shaped like a woman's torso which reveals part of a text by Frederick Kiesler.

Ainsi font...

Eléphants

Cathédrales

(no. 169)